Quattlebaum's Truth

Quattlebaum's Truth

Mark Gross

HARPER & ROW, PUBLISHERS

NEW YORK, EVANSTON, AND LONDON

1817

to god, caroline, bbt, mpj, mbv,
bb, pst, dc, jc, ja, mn, et al.

CONTENTS

Quattlebaum's Truth

I

1. The Rummage Sale

Mr. Quattlebaum liked the way in which religion was beginning to behave in the second half of the twentieth century.

It was difficult to describe the changes. Mr. Quattlebaum's attempts often degenerated into similes and metaphors no less mixed than those upon which religion itself had seemed too often to rely.

It seemed to Mr. Quattlebaum that religion was beginning to practice the best of what it had preached, and to preach fewer of its earlier malpractices.

It seemed to him that religion was beginning to submit to long-recommended surgery after years of salves, pills, gargles, candle-burning and prayers for unlikely miracles.

It seemed to him that religion was beginning to face the kind of fact that confronts the withering prostitute. It had become less attractive. Its market was shrinking. It had to seek new and more dignified sources of support. It had to go more constructively to work within society. And for society. And on society's terms. Or die. For there was no other place to work. And no one else with whom or for whom to work.

At times it seemed to him that religion, on the eve of the twenty-first century, perhaps also had reached the eve of its own twenty-first birthday. There were sudden indications of a maturity long delayed, of a more-than-resigned sense of coming of age, of new interests, of reflective disdain of earlier preoccupations.

At other times it seemed to him that religion was beginning to resemble not so much a young adult as a young adult's father and mother, whose children were now grown, educated and out in the world—helping, as all men must and do, however menially or unwittingly, to push back the constantly receding walls around truth.

Like such a father, religion seemed to be going through its files and discarding or amending those of its records which had become a source of diminishing pride through the years, and those which it had begun to suspect might prove embarrassing to its descendants.

Like such a mother, religion seemed to be facing the painful but plausible task of cleaning house as it never had wanted or been able or forced to clean house before. It seemed to be rewrapping still-valued mementos of childhood but throwing out what now seemed dusty junk. It seemed to be taking another look at long-cherished antiques, and manifesting new ability and inclination to distinguish valid originals from shabby counterfeits.

Indeed it seemed to Mr. Quattlebaum that religion was preparing for a long-postponed rummage sale.

He hoped so. He would be glad to see the stuff out of the house.

He doubted that much of it would sell. And he felt sorry for anyone who might buy. But in either event Mr. Quattlebaum anticipated no dampening of his new optimism. Even if its white elephants should fail to sell, religion now seemed to him less likely to put them back into its closets than to lead them onto Noah's ark with the weasels and the sacred cows—and to push them all out to an invaluable death at sea.

2. *The Damnedest Shame*

There were three things which Mr. Quattlebaum always tried to make clear before being drawn into discussions of religion.

First, he himself was a religious man. If he was also in a sense an agnostic, it was only in the sense and to the extent that every honest and intelligent man, religious or not, must acknowledge that he is powerless to know more than he can know. But he was neither a cynic nor an iconoclast. And he was not an atheist. He had no more respect for presumptuous atheism, which asserted the non-existence of something not yet defined, than for presumptuous "belief" in anything equally undefined.

Second, he disliked sweeping statements, careless generalizations and undefined terms. If he expressed the hopeful surmise that religion might be preparing its white elephants for a rummage sale in the second half of the twentieth century, his friends could be sure that he would be as determined as they to clarify what he meant specifically by religion and by white elephants.

Third, it seemed to Mr. Quattlebaum that no normal man had any right, or even any ability, to be irrational about anything—even about god. He knew, of course, that reasoning could be faulty, that normal men could make mistakes, and that they had and would. Yet he still believed that man's very nature made it impossible for him to be fundamentally irrational about anything—even about god. It seemed to Mr. Quattlebaum that there were good reasons for this belief, and he could be depended upon to review them in some detail.

But before bogging his friends in what at first might strike them as a maze of irrelevant abstractions, Mr. Quattlebaum preferred to state his thesis—which, he rather guessed but could not prove, was shared by most men everywhere, openly or privately.

His thesis was brief:

If a man had neither the right nor the ability to be irrational, yet claimed to "believe" what was irrational, obviously he was only pretending to be irrational.

And about god, it seemed to Mr. Quattlebaum, most men were indeed pretending to be irrational—and even regarding such religious pretense as somehow virtuous. Yet it seemed to him that there was neither truth nor humility nor reverence nor any other virtue in pretense.

Pretense was a sham. It was disgraceful and dishonorable and therefore a shame—and a "damned" shame because it stood rationally condemned by rational men, and thus deservedly doomed.

Pretense seemed in fact to Mr. Quattlebaum the "damnedest" shame of all—to which all other sins or vices were reducible or by which they were cloaked.

Being rational all week, but pretending to be irrational on "the lord's day," seemed to him even more of a damned shame than going to church on one day and sinning all week. Even a week of conventional sin often was more rationally disciplined, he had observed, than were many conventional descriptions of a false and flimsy god by many "virtuous" and "faithful" laymen and by many vocal, second-string theologians.

To him it seemed a damned shame that the pretended irrationality of such men, however blissfully or unwittingly, might well be scandalizing the very god they hoped to serve. For Mr. Quattlebaum, the head most proudly turned from reason was not the head most humbly bowed in prayer. For him the scorning of an honest pagan was the proud act of a man of shallow faith.

To him it seemed a damned shame not to acknowledge that the earnestly rational pagan, agnostic or atheist might be serving god reverently and knowing god well by other names—might be mining the very gold for which theologians pan, or be perhaps a fragment of the very flesh of god still missing from the bones of creed.

It was a damned shame, he thought, to confuse religion itself with irrational, anachronistic ways of discussing it.

It was a damned shame, he thought, to presume a license to be rational at one time and superstitiously irrational at another.

It was a damned shame, he thought, whenever loyalty to creed became loyalty to a pretentiously closed and artificially disconnected mind.

To Mr. Quattlebaum it seemed a damned shame to be loose with words like faith—to dismiss reason as a mere natural faculty while extolling faith as a virtue somehow divinely infused. Did such a thing even exist, he wondered, as a pure metal of faith? And if so was it not softer than that of reason and less precious than their alloy? Or, if there should prove to be no such thing as a pure metal of faith, could there be an alloy at all? To him it seemed a damned shame to fear the very use of reason which might reveal the hidden halves of faith's half-truths and of reason's truths half seen.

To him it seemed a damned shame to be loose with words like revelation—to confuse "revealed" essences with the irrelevant accidents of human language, through which maximum communication could be only approximate at best.

To him it seemed a damned shame that men had become irrational about religion in the first place. But it seemed a still greater shame that they had gone on clinging to ancient, less-than-childish religious notions through so many centuries. To him it seemed that men had become reasonable about everything but reason-in-religion, had become truthful about everything but truth-in-religion, and had ceased to be superstitious about everything but god.

What Mr. Quattlebaum referred to as the ravage of reason in the area of religion, where pretended irrationality had seemed to remain most prevalent and most inexcusably excused, was in his judgment the oldest, the longest-lasting, and indeed the "damnedest" shame in the whole history of man.

And yet, although any of his friends would quickly acknowledge that an extroverted optimism was not his dominant characteristic, he had grown increasingly hopeful in recent years.

Here and there, now and then, a few previously pretended irrationalities about god were being acknowledged and rightfully surrendered to the solvent of thought.

Mr. Quattlebaum being Mr. Quattlebaum, it still seemed to him a damned shame, of course, that such previously pretended irrationalities were being surrendered with such reluctance—and for the most part only in those anguished moments when pressure to admit that the ludicrous was ludicrous seemed greater than the tenacity of residual stubbornness.

But when he said that he liked the way in which religion seemed to be changing its behavior patterns in the second half of the twentieth century, he was really quite sincere.

3. The Whispers of Hope

Religious reform certainly did not seem to Mr. Quattlebaum to be running amuck in the second half of the twentieth century.

He saw no revolution.

But he saw something.

And it seemed to be moving with a little more speed and perceptibility than one usually associates with a mere phase of evolution.

For traditionalist conservatives it was not enough to stir rebellion, but they were pouting. And for Mr. Quattlebaum it was not enough to produce a grin, but he was managing occasional smiles.

There were three reasons why Mr. Quattlebaum was willing to be patient a little longer.

First, of course, he had no choice.

Second, he acknowledged that his society—which had evolved both despite and as a result of centuries of partially irrational religious instruction and practice—was a *sine qua non*. As a good citizen he did not wish to see it suffer a traumatic ungluing in the wake of too-sudden and too-drastic change.

And third, he felt within his very bones that this time the cause of religious reform would not be stopped in its tracks, but would continue to inch ahead to a series of logical victories despite hell and high water. How could you get 'em back on the farm, now that they'd seen Paree?

It was quite apparent to Mr. Quattlebaum that the "image" of the church was changing faster than it ever had changed before. What such an image might become was still much less apparent than what it was ceasing to be, but for the moment he was consoled by its ceasing to be some of the things which it had been. Slums had to be removed before new structures could rise, and it seemed to him that a sort of mental slum-razing was clearly a part of the newly changing image of the church.

"Image" had become a loose and generally unreliable cliché to which Mr. Quattlebaum really preferred not to resort. It was being used too often as a substitute for thinking, and even as a vaccination against thought. A bright coat of paint could give a house a good image even if termites had all but removed the floors and stairs. Image had become a favorite concept of public relations counselors, concerned with creating favorable surface impressions even of their most detestable clients. Images were dangerous. In the minds of the relatively ignorant and of the relatively well-informed alike, images were the too-quickly-freezing impressions of the unexamined and the unreviewed.

Inevitably, however, images were in fact a part of the raw material with which a hurried era did some of its thinking. And they were not wholly devoid of validity. If the mere mention of an institution evoked varying impressions in various minds, it was because that institution actually presented a variety of characteristics, however mixed and unanalyzed, by which to be impressed. And it was a sort of presumed average of such impressions that men referred to as "the image" of such an institution.

It was in this sense that Mr. Quattlebaum and many of his contemporaries referred to the changing image of the church. There was no single, identical image to which each referred, because the impressions of each were necessarily somewhat subjective. But because the impressions of each were also somewhat objective, they partially overlapped and coincided. There was not only a diversity of individual images—but also a smaller, single, shared image—of a changing church.

It seemed to Mr. Quattlebaum that there was an increasingly swift retreat, along an increasingly broad front, from a "fundamentalism" which had been in no proper sense fundamental.

While Protestants, Roman Catholics, Jews, agnostics, pagans and atheists seemed in a sense more confused than ever, it appeared to Mr. Quattlebaum to be a more honest and thus more hopeful confusion. Perhaps, he thought, it was not unlike the temporarily increased confusion of a neurotic or psychotic in the early stages of intensive therapy. Old conflicts between reason and long-pretended adherence to seemingly irrational beliefs had not yet been resolved, but they were being brought out into the open for examination in healthier perspectives.

It seemed to Mr. Quattlebaum that there were now fewer glib references and less lip service to "miracles" which seemed out of key with reason, and less "going along" with the uncomprehended in unreflective silence.

Two previously warring groups, for example—one which had defended to the point of childish anger every humanly translated assertion in every alleged book of the Bible, and one which sneeringly had dismissed the Bible as a mere record of ancestral naïveté —now were beginning to pay more attention to a third group, which had gathered from across the borders of traditional creed and sect to make quiet, unemotional, respectably scientific studies of what the Bible really was.

The religious wars were not over, but on virtually every battlefield Mr. Quattlebaum could see groups of combatants smiling and waving little white flags at each other in a seemingly declining fear of reprimand by commanding officers. Like maturing members of college fraternities and sororities, warring churchmen seemed to be acknowledging that much of what they had called doctrinal or organizational loyalty in fact had been snobbery. They still had not lost their desire to belong, to be accepted, and to be right; but they seemed to be approaching a realization that there was some right and some wrong in each of their groups.

A few Protestants and Roman Catholics were becoming Jews.

A few Jews were becoming Protestants or Roman Catholics.

A few Protestants were becoming Roman Catholics.

A few Roman Catholics were becoming Protestants.

And a few of the previously unaffiliated were joining one group or another.

But much more frequent were the instances of quiet disaffiliation or desertion, or at least of individual armistice.

And Mr. Quattlebaum disagreed with those who saw this phenomenon as a deplorable wave of atheism.

He saw it as a hopeful wave of increased sincerity and intellectual honesty.

Many non-Catholics were seeking acceptable ways to trade their diversities of creed for the relative singleness of belief which had been a hallmark of the Catholic. They realized that conflicting truths ultimately were impossible.

But many Catholics simultaneously were seeking acceptable ways to bring prematurely closed issues out of committee and back onto the floor for previously overruled discussion. They, too, realized that conflicting truths were ultimately impossible. But they were beginning to admit the survival of conflicts which had not been resolved but only buried—while still very much alive.

It seemed to Mr. Quattlebaum that fewer and fewer of his Catholic friends were mistaking historically accidental practices of their church for parts of its essence.

They seemed to be collecting more coins, stamps and butterflies, and fewer medals, scapulars, holy cards and souvenirs touched to relics.

There was less incense, less boycotting of movies and censoring of books, less anguished squeezing of beads at football games, less sprinkling of holy water.

Articles entitled "Back to Thomism" and advertisements for lamp bases filled with miracle water from Lourdes had all but disappeared from Catholic publications.

There were fewer bingo cards, fewer raffle tickets, fewer mentions of 600-day indulgences, fewer anachronistic paintings of an exposed physical heart hanging on living room walls, fewer plastic statues mounted above automobile instrument panels, and fewer billboard references to families which stayed together because they prayed together (possibly because so many which had hadn't and so many which hadn't had).

Mr. Quattlebaum had watched a growing awareness, followed by an "official" acknowledgment, that not eating meat on Fridays had been a man-made, and by no means the most important man-made, form of useful self-mortification—and that there was also value in self-vivification.

It seemed to him that the traditionally automatic exclamation of most Catholics upon learning of the mere existence of virtually any Catholic couple who had bred eight or more children ("My, what a nice Catholic family!") was now assuming an improved connotation. He welcomed an apparently broadening recognition that "god's plan" or "the natural law" might provide as much moral sanction of two or four well-behaved and well-educated children as of fourteen illiterate brats. More and more of his Catholic friends were waiting at least to be introduced to the members of a given household before pronouncing it "a nice Catholic family."

In his own lifetime had come a sharp decline in Catholic criticism of Catholic parents whose Catholic children were in non-Catholic schools, and an increase in the number of Catholics who wondered whether or why there should be Catholic schools at all.

And even in Catholic schools—where he believed too many catechisms had expressed an "orthodoxy" which was neither interesting, understandable nor defensibly orthodox—he felt quite sure that he saw a greater striving for "secularistic" scholars and a declining acceptance of "holy" dunces. He observed that geography texts were bearing less and less resemblance to travel folders for abandoned missions, and that American history texts were beginning to devote as many pages to World War I as to Mother Seton.

Mr. Quattlebaum was hearing fewer references by his Catholic friends to a fiery hell, to a half-way house of purgatory, or to a heaven in which they and their relatives would be bothered by only a few non-Catholics at worst.

He was hearing fewer references to St. Jude, the Little Flower, the Infant of Prague and even to the Blessed Virgin Mary—and more and more questioning into the whetherness and nature of god.

All in all it seemed to Mr. Quattlebaum that more and more of his church-going friends, Catholic and non-Catholic alike, had stopped thanking god that they were not as other men.

It seemed to him that they had begun to face up to the fact that possession of "the whole truth" was something to which none of them could yet lay honest claim—with or without the alleged assurances of any church.

What Mr. Quattlebaum found most hopeful was not the mere fact that men were admitting that the image of their churches seemed odd and incongruous in the second half of the twentieth century after Jesus. Nor would he have been satisfied by their determination merely to improve that image. He did not believe that such seeming oddities and incongruities could be resolved or hidden or that men should try to resolve or hide them, even if they could, by false or superficial ecumenism or by mere "public relations."

He did not believe that anything of value could be gained by rearranging oddities, incongruities or even accuracies as if they were a bowl of four-day-old flowers, hiding the bedraggled blossoms behind the fresher blooms and buds.

What Mr. Quattlebaum found most hopeful was man's apparent new determination not merely to make his churches look modern, rational and trustworthy, but to make them become in fact modern, rational and trustworthy.

He did not believe that any church could become in fact a modern, rational, trustworthy institution if it neglected to examine any evidence which might in any way be relevant to matters about which it might pose conclusions or hypotheses. And in none of the words of Moses, Buddha, Jesus, Mohammed, Luther, Mary Baker Eddy or anyone else—words chosen at specific times for specific audiences—could he find even the slightest excuse for excluding from men's honest consideration so much as a scrap of evidence for or against any proposition or belief.

It seemed to Mr. Quattlebaum that this had become the conviction of most men.

It seemed to him that more and more men would refuse to tolerate any withholding of evidence, or the condemnation of any conclusion or point of view on the basis of poor evidence or none, in the previously over-privileged courts of their churches.

Mr. Quattlebaum was increasingly hopeful because it seemed to him that more and more men were deciding to stop begging basic questions—and to stop pretending respect for those who did.

4. The Big Begged Questions

"Upon the basis of what evidence," Mr. Quattlebaum would ask at lunch, "and at the neglect of what contrary evidence have most churches characterized our universe as a vast battleground of dualisms locked in basic conflict?"

"Why," he would ask, "have most of our churches seen this as a universe full of pairs of warring worlds?"

Jabbing the air with carrot sticks to punctuate his litany, he would ask:

Why a next world versus this world?

Why a world in which to seek personal salvation versus a world in which to become socially involved?

Why a world of time and space versus a world of eternity?

Why a supernatural world versus a natural world?

Why a world of faith versus a world of reason?

Why a world of inherently unfathomable mystery versus a world more limitedly comprehensible by reason?

Why a Catholic world versus a non-Catholic world?

Why a Christian world versus a non-Christian world?

Why a world of religious thought versus a world of pagan, agnostic or atheistic thought?

Why a material world versus a spiritual world?

Why a "sacred" world versus a "profane" world?

Did such mutually exclusive worlds really exist at all?

Mr. Quattlebaum could find no evidence that they did.

Were such essentially opposed and warring worlds explicitly asserted or necessarily implied in the essence of any religious creed?

He honestly believed that they were not.

There had been evidence for at least 2600 years—evidence which Mr. Quattlebaum thought no modern, rational, trustworthy church could wish to overlook—that notions of such fundamentally opposed and warring worlds were no more than what logicians called false dichotomies: concepts partitioned into pairs of unreal opposites.

He felt that the traditional preaching of such imagined separatism, of such imagined exclusivism, of such imagined estrangement of warring worlds, had been a damned shame. He felt in fact that it had been presumptuous segregationism in its most basic and most fundamentally irreligious form.

A "sacred" world versus a "profane" world?

How, Mr. Quattlebaum wanted to know, could one assert that "holy" and "profane" were validly, meaningfully opposed if one could find only a circular definition of either word?

Yet *kadosh*, a Hebrew word for "holiness," had denoted service to others and separation from the profane.

And *profanus*, the Latin word for "profane," had meant "outside the temple"—separation from the sacred.

To say that the profane, secular, worldly or temporal denoted whatever was not sacred, hallowed, holy or divine—or that the sacred, hallowed, holy or divine denoted whatever was not profane, secular, worldly or temporal—was in Mr. Quattlebaum's opinion to say nothing at all. It was merely to recite meaningless, question-begging denotations of two concepts—but to point to valid connotations or essences of neither.

How, then, he would ask, can anyone be sure that what generally is called profane, secular, worldly or temporal pertains any less to god, proceeds any less from god, or in fact partakes any less of god's very nature than does that which generally is called sacred, hallowed, holy or divine?

How, then, can one be sure, he would ask, whether those things which we presume to distinguish as profane and divine are in fact opposed, disparate and immiscible?

How can one be sure that they are not actually congenial, compatible and related?

Who is to say, and upon the basis of what evidence, that such presumed opposites cannot be perhaps in some sense or degree even uniform, equivalent, selfsame or identical?

Mr. Quattlebaum neither sought nor enjoyed the vicarious pleasures of the habitual iconoclast or of the cynical debunker. To do harm to any valid dignity or utility of a church was among the last things of which he could wish to be guilty.

If he seriously doubted that the universe had been "created" in the generally naïve sense of that word, or that god was an anthropomorphic father prototype, or that there were such physical places as heaven and hell, or that many if any "miracles" had been truly paranatural, it was not at all because he presumed either the non-existence of a god or the impossibility of relationships between a god and men.

On the contrary, the fact that he could not buy much of what our churches had been marketing as religion was a result of his encounters with those very pieces of evidence, recorded through some 2600 years, which had prompted him to suspect that there might be a god indeed, and one with which men might enjoy a relationship more intimate, more necessary and more unavoidable than that which most of our churches had postulated or had seemed even to imagine.

Actually, Mr. Quattlebaum would ask, have not our churches outdone our atheists in contributing to the blunting and even to the cheapening of such concepts as god, creation, holy spirit, natural law, incarnation, redemption, salvation, resurrection, ascension, assumption and the like?

For it seemed to him that many of our churches had been saying to every man:

"These are mysteries, my child. Not merely mysteries of the moment. But mysteries inherently and eternally. Mysteries which in their very nature are and must remain sacred untouchables. Mysteries necessarily and by very definition beyond the reach of human comprehension. So question not. Probe not. Study not. Accept."

Mr. Quattlebaum intensely disliked that sort of thing. It rubbed him the wrong way. He believed that every man in fact was rubbed the wrong way by any invitation to suspend his natural activity of thought within any arena of human experience or speculation.

And so he had stayed away from the arenas where the smug and self-righteous had gathered to watch honest and dishonest atheists thrown indiscriminately to the lions of intellectual dishonesty. He could not believe that such an atheist was less a martyr than the earlier Christian or the later Jew. Each had been the victim of uncharitable ignorance.

The sin of many atheists, it seemed to Mr. Quattlebaum, had been not their rejection of the ill-defined (which rejection he regarded as in fact a virtue) but rather their arbitrarily premature denial of the very existence of something which might yet be defined.

But he felt that the sin of many churches had been no less mortal and no more venial: an equally arbitrary, equally premature acceptance of the undefined, and an even-more-objectionable insistence that definition of "sacred mysteries" was neither desirable nor inherently possible.

Atheist and church alike, it seemed to Mr. Quattlebaum, had been guilty of the sin of presumption.

Each had begged the big questions.

His sympathies had lain more with those atheists who had confined their negativism to attacks upon the anachronisms and logical fallacies of many churches than with those churches which had asked men merely to "have faith" in clouded concepts which they had done relatively little to clarify.

But Mr. Quattlebaum felt almost certain that his new hopefulness was justified. More and more men were trying to look more deeply into "sacred mysteries" than ever before. He believed they would continue to question and to probe and to seek greater understanding of such "mysteries" because, as men, they simply must. He believed it was their very nature to think. He knew that men could and often did fail to reach rationally sound conclusions; but he felt that it was literally beyond man's power to make himself fundamentally irrational, that he could only pretend to be irrational, and that in pretense there was neither virtue nor knowledge.

He knew that men could and often did accept as hypotheses propositions which they did not fully comprehend. But he believed that at no instant could any man accept the incomprehensible, because he believed that at such an instant no man could be a man. He believed that even an interim hypothesis could be accepted tentatively only for its apparent or possible reasonableness.

And so he felt confident that men would, because men must, seek needle and thread with which to mend their ripped and ragged views of god.

He believed men would, because he believed men must, seek to distill religious concepts and strive to extract from their religious notions residues of clear, pure truth—by endeavoring to drive off the noxious gases of superstition and to filter out the gummy colloids of contradiction and accidental irrelevance.

As in all undertakings of such magnitude, men would need all the expert help they could get.

But who and where were the "religion experts" or the "specialists in god"?

The theologians?

"O good lord," groaned Mr. Quattlebaum. "They need more help than anyone!"

5. The Queen Pretender

Mr. Quattlebaum never had joined in any general attack upon theology as such or upon theologians as a group. He refused to become identified with the injustice of mass indictment or with the pointless negativism of recrimination.

Moreover he was aware that in recent decades more and more theologians had seemed to be trying to separate the essential wheat of traditional religious beliefs from the chaff of superstition, contradiction and irrelevance. It seemed to him that they had been acknowledging failures of their predecessors, gaining keen insights into the nature of such failures, and retooling for new and better approaches to the problems of god.

And of course, as Mr. Quattlebaum readily admitted, if theology had not succeeded in solving all its problems, neither had physics or economics or any of the other branches of science. And the fact that no branch of science had yet completed its part of the human quest of truth was no cause for alarm.

He felt there would be cause for alarm only if any branch of science should fail to recognize that journey's end was still far off, or that new evidence gathered within each branch of science inevitably would become increasingly relevant to, interrelated with and contingent upon new evidence gathered within all the other branches of science.

To exempt theology or any other branch of science from any essential principle, practice or discipline of science would have been, in Mr. Quattlebaum's opinion, illegitimately arbitrary and gratuitous. He believed that theology was either a branch of science, privileged to use the proper tools and methods of science and properly subject to its universal disciplines, or a field of activity no more entitled to scientific status than an international poetry circle.

He saw theology as a science but a science almost without scientists. And thus he saw theologians who were true scientists as scientists almost without a science.

But it was enough to build upon.

And he was grateful for those genuinely scientific theologians who were trying to research and to search, to speculate and to hypothesize, and to scrutinize the findings of geology, biochemistry, psychology and all the other branches of science for new clues to the nature of the universe, of man and of god, and for new insights into possible god-man relationships.

But he was not grateful for those more numerous pseudo-scientists who called themselves theologians but who could produce only the credentials of night watchmen, sitting gun-in-hand with little boxes of "infinite truth" in their laps, seeming to defy any scientist-prowler to make a gesture of aggressive heresy.

Such clods and bores, in Mr. Quattlebaum's judgment, had little of importance to contribute to man's search for truth. They seemed content to go on mumbling repetitiously that the marigolds and buttercups had come up again this year, still manifesting unswerving fidelity to "the natural law," still beautifully reconfirming an unchanging god whose wondrous inscrutability excused us all from further thought and asked of us no more than redundant meditation upon the goodness, omnipresence and omniscience of an undefined and indefinable blob.

Such pseudo-theologians did not play, because they were incompetent to play, any scientific role according to scientific rule.

Surely, Mr. Quattlebaum insisted, they did not even begin to comprehend the structure of the sciences—or they would not have referred to theology, as they often did, as "queen" of the sciences —or to philosophy, the real mistress of the sciences, as a mere "handmaiden" of theology.

To call the very mistress of the sciences a mere handmaiden of a sub-science seemed to him no less bizarre than to call highway engineering the mere handmaiden of bulldozers and cement mixers.

It seemed to Mr. Quattlebaum that these pseudo-theologians had plunged presumptuously into post-graduate work after only a smattering of undergraduate training. They had tried to play Bach before learning the scale. With pitifully small knowledge of the "natural," how, Mr. Quattlebaum wondered, could they pontificate on the "supernatural"? Without knowledge of nature, how could they know what if anything was beyond nature?

How, for example, can they speak meaningfully of a god who is an uncaused cause, he would ask, unless they have made a prior study of the meaning of causation itself? How can they speak so blithely about man's "physical body" and "spiritual soul" without prior philosophical consideration of mind, matter and at least a few of the difficulties to be encountered in any honest attempt to explain mind-body relationships? What satisfaction can an honest and intelligent man find in permitting himself to babble on about what an undefined god did or did not do, in or out of time, if such a man has given no prior philosophical consideration to the nature of time itself?

Nothing seemed more obvious to Mr. Quattlebaum than that any "truth" which was expressed in vague, frozen, dull or mysterious concepts was, to that extent, a stagnant, trite or fragmentary "truth"—and could become no richer, broader or deeper until the basic concepts in which it was expressed had become sharper and more broadly and deeply understood.

And he believed that the sharpening of such basic concepts as time, space, cause, mind and matter was the proper province of philosophy, mistress of the sciences, constantly striving for greater conceptual refinement in the light of the findings of her sub-sciences.

Like each of her sister sub-sciences, from astrophysics to zymology, theology dealt with a single principal area of study: god and religion. And however "royal" an area of study this might be, Mr. Quattlebaum insisted that it was still only one area and thus without excuse for pretense to the very throne of science.

He insisted that any "theologian's" failure or refusal to renounce theology's unrightful claim to the throne of science was itself an abdication of the theologian's rightful duties to science.

It seemed to him that he insisted only upon the obvious: that if theology, chemistry or any other branch of science failed or refused to acknowledge and perform its rightful duties to science-as-a-whole, it could not be a science at all. It could only pretend to be.

6. The Rightful Monarch

If there had been any point in choosing a "queen" of the sciences, Mr. Quattlebaum would have nominated philosophy without question or hesitation. There was a completely proper sense in which it could be said that philosophy always had been and must remain the rightful monarch in the realm of science, *per omnia saecula saeculorum.*

On the other hand, to call philosophy the "queen" of the sciences was to suggest a separateness or apartness from the other sciences, and perhaps a sort of sovereign potentiality for pulling rank on them, which were not at all characteristic of philosophy.

If philosophy was a queen, she was more enlightened and compassionate, more patient and just, more "at one" with her subjects and more dependent upon them, than any monarch whom Mr. Quattlebaum could recall.

Philosophy was more than the queen of the sciences. She was one of them. But not separately. She was their total.

Philosophy was science itself.

Philosophy was science-as-a-whole.

Philosophy in Mr. Quattlebaum's judgment was the chief scientific investigator into the facts and principles of all reality: being, knowledge, logic, god, man, the "divine," the "profane," ethics, aesthetics and all the rest.

And the areas of study which men called sciences—physics, physiology, linguistics, theology and all the others—were philosophy's sub-sciences or branches, her laborers, her sharecroppers.

Mr. Quattlebaum saw philosophy as the model monarch, and her society of sub-sciences as the model society. Without them she was nothing, and without her they were nothing. She fed them well, and they fed her. She educated them, and they educated her. She protected them, and they protected her. She worked them hard, and they worked her hard. As they prospered, she prospered. As she prospered, they prospered. Working together under the same laws of thought and with the same precision tools, the sub-sciences constantly sought new truths; and in their light philosophy sought constantly to refine the hypothetical definitions of such basic concepts as time, space, cause, matter and mind. Whatever the sub-sciences found they gave to philosophy, confident that she would return to them more than they had given. And so she did. But only because of what she had received from them.

Nothing so deeply satisfied Mr. Quattlebaum as to watch philosophy studying the findings of each of her sub-sciences, sorting and analyzing them, ordering and classifying them, testing them and integrating them with the findings of the other sub-sciences, looking always for new rational relationships, insights and hypotheses to pass back to her deputy sciences.

Philosophy's perspective was the world's broadest. Philosophy's vantage point was the world's highest. Philosophy was the world's only clearing house for all the findings of all her deputy sciences, from whom she received and to whom she gave back truth which became larger with each receiving and with each giving.

Philosophy and her sub-sciences were the funnels of discovery, the media of all new knowledge. Philosophy was the way men continued to learn from what they continued to learn.

It seemed quite clear to Mr. Quattlebaum that philosophy could exempt none of her deputy sciences, not even theology, from their common ground-rule disciplines. To make exceptions or play favorites would have been a breach of reason. And reason seemed the very essence of philosophy's society of sciences.

A single dispensation from the discipline of reason could have thrown the entire society of the sciences into fatal chaos, as the tiniest air bubble in the bloodstream could cause death, or as fertilization of the tiniest egg could cause pregnancy. And Mr. Quattlebaum was convinced that there was no such thing as a tolerably moderate degree of death, pregnancy or licensed irrationality.

And yet, while philosophy could dispense neither herself nor any of her sub-sciences from the discipline of reason, he observed that philosophy was not afraid to make mistakes. She seemed aware that it was out of one day's mistakes that the next day's truth must come —truth which could become the following day's error only if supplanted by still larger truth.

Hence philosophy's insistence upon the freedom of her deputy sciences, freedom from everything except the laws of thought. And even the laws of thought did not restrict freedom. The safeguarding of reason was freedom's purpose. To be free was to be treated reasonably and to be permitted to behave reasonably. To be a slave was to be restricted unreasonably.

In order to reduce their ignorance, men had to experiment. Those experiments which failed to confirm their hypotheses still served the cause of truth by demonstrating what was false. Mr. Quattlebaum felt quite certain that, while the road to hell might or might not be paved with good intentions, most roads to truth were paved with valuable mistakes.

And this, he believed, was why philosophy and her responsible sub-sciences did not waste time pointlessly lamenting the fact of human fallibility. They recognized it as an essential of the predicament of man. They employed and exploited it. They used it as a valuable tool. And they met the occasional claim to infallibility with a kind and silent smile, believing that the man with a truly infallible proposition had the least to fear from rational cross-examination.

7. *The Timid Science*

Why, Mr. Quattlebaum wondered, had one of the sciences appeared more timid than the others?

Why had theology seemed to fear the use of its quite proper freedom to experiment, its quite proper freedom to make mistakes in the testing of hypotheses?

Why had theology seemed to fear its very obligation to risk those temporary mistakes without which no science could honestly hope to avoid mistakes more harmfully enduring?

And why had theology seemed reticent to examine and slow to acknowledge possible theological implications in the dramatic new findings of its sister sciences?

Had not theology really feared that such examination might yield new perspectives and new intellectual insights—which, in turn, might inspire plausible new hypotheses concerning the nature of god—which, in turn, might threaten traditional hypotheses which too many theologians had found it "divinely" comforting to regard as relatively finished business?

Had too many theologians become so nearly paranoiac in their devotion to traditional religious hypotheses that the possibility of conflicting evidence threatened their vestigial ability to ambulate and communicate within a society of rational men?

"If so," Mr. Quattlebaum often said, "let both the therapy and the prophylaxis begin"—not only for those theologians who had been shy, withdrawn and uncommunicative with their fellow scientists, but also for those millions of equally sincere and self-thwarting laymen whose willingness and ability to pretend to be irrational about religion had been all but exhausted.

It seemed to Mr. Quattlebaum that the mental health of all men depended upon their ability and opportunity to ambulate and communicate reasonably within the society of the sciences as well as within the society of men—if indeed there was really any fundamental difference between the two.

Perhaps it was that funny thing which had happened on his last night at college, years ago, which had provided the genesis of his conviction that, as a science, theology was no less dependent than any other science upon all of its sister sciences and upon the master science of philosophy—and that neither theology nor mankind could afford the dubious luxury of clinging to a partial past in fear of a filling future.

8. The Baccalaureate

Sitting there in the candlelight among the potted ferns, none of the graduates or proud parents had any reason to suspect that this would be very different from any other baccalaureate.

A virtually unknown speaker, introduced by the university president as "a very well-known member of a growing group of progressive theologians," had just cleared his throat.

"I assume," he had begun, "that all of us who are gathered here tonight on this memorable occasion share the belief that our physical bodies, our spiritual souls and indeed the entirety of our vast and unfathomable universe were created by an equally unfathomable and omnipotent person, power or entity which we call god."

And right then was when it had happened.

A graduate had risen in front of his second-row seat and raised his hand. The startled speaker had yielded the floor with a charitably prompt nod toward the rude, mortarboarded silhouette.

"I know this isn't the right time for questions," the student had begun rather irrefutably. "And I don't really know very much about god and all that. I've been majoring in animal husbandry with a minor in English lit. But I had this roommate who had this argument about god creating the universe, and it always seemed pretty good to me. And since you say we probably all agree about god creating the universe and our bodies and souls and all that, I thought maybe you'd like to comment on it right now. Because, honestly, I don't think a lot of people are too clear about some of the things they say they believe about religion. I know I'm not. Sometimes I feel like an awful hypocrite."

"Well, frankly, sometimes I do, too; but I'll be happy to try to help," the compassionate theologian had said as whispering parents were discovering from their sons and daughters that the interruptor, who "always does things like this," was Marvin Breedlove from Nebraska.

"Well," Marvin had continued, "the argument went something like this. 'Created' is a verb. And verbs are all about time. They are past, present or future. Well, if time is a part of the universe which god created, then there couldn't have been any time before it was created. There couldn't have been any time for god to create it in. So how do we know we can accurately use 'created,' or any other past-tense verb, to describe whatever 'happened' to the universe in the 'beginning'? How do we even know there was a beginning?

"Then there was this other part of the argument which said but if time did exist before god created the universe, then time couldn't really have been part of the universe god created. So maybe god didn't create everything, at least not time. Or maybe, if god created the universe, whatever really happened was a lot different from what a lot of people say happened. Or did god really do anything? I mean it's sort of confusing and all, and it all kind of makes me wonder."

The speaker had seemed genuinely pleased by the strange interruption.

"Actually, the young man's point is well taken," he had said, turning from Marvin to face the entire audience again. "Let me just say that . . . "

"Pardon me, sir," Marvin had broken in again, "but there was this one other thing which maybe you might want to comment on at the same time. I mean about god creating man with both a body and a soul. My roommate also used to ask how could we be so sure of that? He said we never really experience anything, even what we call physical bodies, except in our minds, so that how could we be so sure there's really anything else? I mean anyone has to admit it sure seems like there are physical bodies and matter and all, but anyone also has to admit it's awful hard to imagine how two things so different as mind and matter can actually touch each other. And yet they sure seem to have an influence on each other—if they're really different things, that is.

"This roommate—I keep mentioning him like he was god or something, but he did have some pretty sharp ideas—anyway, he said that some philosopher—Descartes, I think it was—the one who doubted so many things and then believed just what he couldn't keep doubting—got himself into a mess trying to figure out just which tiny little piece of flesh or a gland or something was the place where mind and matter actually could touch each other.

"But anyway, things like these make me wonder if we really can be so sure, like you said in your very first sentence, which I interrupted, that god created the whole universe—or so sure he really created men who are partly physical and partly mental. And since you're kind of an expert in things like this, I thought maybe this would be a good chance to find out. I'm sorry I interrupted you, though."

"Not at all," the theologian had resumed. "You raise excellent points. You had a good roommate. I hope he runs into many of my fellow theologians. He could give many of them some good pointers. Let me try to answer you this way . . . "

He had slipped the paper clip back onto his prepared manuscript and shoved it aside. Resting his elbows against the lectern and thoughtfully biting his lower lip, he had frowned and said:

"There are many of us—Protestants, Catholics and Jews alike—and others—who believe sincerely and on the basis of what seems good evidence that a supreme and ineffable entity which we call god seemingly speaks to man, or succeeds in suggesting to many men at least the possibility of god's existence, in three ways: through men's ability to reason, through those millions of apparently ordered natural phenomena which constitute men's environment, and less frequently through startling instances of what many of us have come to call direct, divine revelation.

"But why, in the course of man's close study and analysis of such alleged messages from god, do they often seem so indistinct or blurred? I believe there are several possible reasons.

"First, there is the communication difficulty. Even if we call the transmitter divine, with full power and perfect fidelity and frequency, man's receiving sets are humanly imperfect. They may miss parts of a possible message. They may pick up crackling static along with possible parts of a possible message. Some theologians have not always been careful to distinguish possible static from possible message-proper. In effect they have said: 'Here is a recording of a message from god. Since it comes from god, everything in it must be true. Don't change a thing.' So even some of the whines and squeals and crackles of static may have been mistaken for possible sounds of heaven. Worthless static may have been classified naïvely as divine revelation. Blurs may have been mistaken for a part of the possible essence of things blurred.

"Second, there is the difficulty of language. If Moses, for example, was spoken to by god, and if he understood what was said to him, he was of course addressed in humanly understandable language. Even an omniscient linguist could transmit no more through any language than that language itself could carry, just as the strongest heart could push no more blood than the arteries and veins could carry, and just as the largest refinery could transmit no more oil than the pipes could transport. Therefore it would seem that neither the formulation, transmission nor receipt in humanly understandable language of messages, even 'from god,' could transcend the limitations of such language. And reception of such limited messages is further affected by the human recipient's still-more-imperfect comprehension of the meanings of the words of his own language.

"Add to these difficulties the erosions and dilutions and evaporations and other transformations of languages and their meanings through the centuries, and one begins to perceive how staggeringly enormous is the task of men who seek, conscientiously and scientifically, to separate 'divine essence' from merely accidental linguistic irrelevance in any allegedly direct messages from god to man.

"Again, therefore, let me say that, in their examinations of possible god-to-man messages, conscientiously thoughtful men will struggle stubbornly to avoid careless confusion of the inevitable blurs of communication and human language with the essence of things blurred.

"There is still another difficulty. Any direct 'revelation' which may have been made by god to men centuries ago was made to men who had attained a certain level of aggregate knowledge. No such 'revelation' contained any then-pointless reference to then-unknown nuclear fission, interplanetary travel, hotdogs or twentieth-century concepts of time, space or mind-body relationships—phenomena which plausibly could punctuate any 'divine revelation' which might occur today. If today's human understanding of such concepts as time, space, creation, causation, matter and mind are closer to the truth than yesterday's, and if they will be still more advanced tomorrow, must we not be guided by such new findings or hypotheses of the sciences when we appraise old statements of religious 'truth'?

"If Jesus fed a multitude with bread and fish rather than with beer and pretzels, it was at least partly because that particular multitude was ignorant of beer and pretzels—not because bread and fish are inherently more 'divine.' If god speaks to us, it is in languages and in concepts which we understand, and not in languages or in concepts which we do not understand—or god simply is not speaking to us at all.

"Surely those of us who do not seek to distinguish the essences of possible god-to-man messages from the merely irrelevant accidents of human language and communication are not worthy to be called scientists or even mature men.

"And so I would say again to the young man here in the second row that it would seem to me that—what is your name, sir?"

"Marvin Breedlove."

"Breedlove? I would say again to Mr. Breedlove, and to all of you, that the honest, questioning spirit which Mr. Breedlove has displayed here tonight is more vital to the success of man's continuing search for truth, including truth about god, than is anything which I had planned to say to you.

"No, Mr. Breedlove, there is not a theological Santa Claus. We theologians are not yet able to fill your stocking with incontestable definitions of what we mean by divine creation—or even by divine. I wish we had time to explore some of the very 'exciting' new notions of god, if that isn't too 'secular' an expression—some of the truly exciting new notions of god which more and more of my associates are finding the courage to examine in public.

"But perhaps the most important thing about a few of these 'progressive' theologians is this:

"They have ceased to assume that the so-called 'supernatural' is in its very nature necessarily beyond the ultimate understanding of men. They have ceased to assume that the 'supernatural' is an area of truth whose very essence segregates it from the area of what we call 'merely natural' truth. They have ceased to assume that the 'supernatural' can be studied most profitably in quiet little rooms shut off from studies of the natural. They are beginning to acknowledge that they cannot really call a thing supernatural (beyond the natural) unless they first understand the natural itself—well enough to be certain that a 'supernatural' is really beyond it.

"Speaking only for myself," the speaker had concluded, "and as a theologian—at least I try to be a theologian—I would say that for theology, no less than for the other sciences, the questions 'Why?' and 'How?' and 'What?' must always be viewed as valid questions in any context—questions ultimately and implicitly answerable by men, no matter how terribly far off the real answers may be.

"In other words, it seems to me that to grant the intelligibility of one area of truth, while insisting upon the fundamental, essential unintelligibility of another, would be to destroy confidence in intelligibility itself.

"We will all agree that this has been a rather unusual evening. But for me, at least, it also has been an unusually stimulating one. I hope you have found it so. May god bless this graduating class. And may god—whoever or whatever he or it may be—bless the world with courageous leadership by its members in the years ahead. Thank you and good night."

Marvin had hurried back to his room. He couldn't get his diploma the next day unless he turned in a late paper by eight in the morning—about new cures for avian trichomoniasis and their effect upon the death rate of North American turkeys.

Quattlebaum had gone down to Niccolini's for a couple of postbaccalaureate beers with a few of the other graduates whose parents hadn't been able to come for commencement.

"Four solid years of college," he had thought, on his last walk back to the dorm, "and that stupid Marvin Breedlove still hasn't learned to keep his mouth shut."

In the hotel elevator, going up to his room, the guest-theologian had snapped his fingers at a sudden afterthought.

"Damn. There at the end I should have said something about the ultimate idiocy of trying to define *religious* truth before trying to define *truth itself.*"

II

9. *The Credentials of Truth*

Quattlebaum got his diploma and went back home and got a job and a wife and children and problems and then, one night, he began to reflect upon something which he had read to his little boy before putting him to bed and hearing his prayers.

"Mother, may I go out to swim?"

"Yes, my darling daughter. Hang your clothes on a hickory limb. But don't go near the water."

It was "true," Mr. Quattlebaum mused, that the daughter had her mother's permission to swim. Yet it also was "true" that she did not.

It was "true" that the conflict might be resolved calmly. Yet it also was "true" that the mother and her darling daughter might have a violent argument.

"What is truth," Mr. Quattlebaum asked himself, "and what makes it true, and how do you recognize it when you see it, and how do you test and prove it?"

It was true, he thought, that nearly everyone had a general, loose agreement with nearly everyone else as to what truth was. Yet it also was true that nearly everyone disagreed with nearly everyone else, at one time or another, as to what specifically was true.

Nearly everyone seemed to agree on the truth of things which were "reliable" and which "really existed"—on the truth of events which were "actual" and which "undoubtedly transpired"—and on the truth of propositions which were "valid," "in conformity with the facts," "genuinely correct" and certainly "free from error."

Yet nearly everyone seemed also to disagree with nearly everyone else, at one time or another, as to whether a particular thing, event or proposition was "really true," "actually factual," or "certainly valid."

But to Mr. Quattlebaum this state of affairs seemed clearly more hopeful than hopeless. For nearly everyone was striving for agreement rather than for disagreement. Nearly everyone was appealing to an objective rather than to a subjective standard of truth. Nearly everyone was saying: "Don't take my word for it. Look at the facts. Look at the record. Look at something beyond my biases, my prejudices, my limited knowledge."

Such a man might not mean all that he said. He might want his side to win. But he seemed to know that, while the other side might not bow to his side, it usually would bow to the disinterested third party of truth—or at least to what it believed to be truth.

So, while men often disagreed as to which things were true, most of them seemed to agree that there was such a thing as truth—and that a true thing, event or proposition was true independently of any particular man's awareness or acknowledgment of it.

Mr. Quattlebaum was quite aware that acceptance of the truth of specific things, events or propositions was anything but universal. But the appeal to men of truth itself—men's apparent desire to know the "real" truth—did seem universal, or nearly so.

Whatever else truth might be, it seemed to Mr. Quattlebaum something which nearly everyone sought and respected, and upon which nearly everyone would agree if all could view the same pieces of evidence in the same contexts, from the same perspectives, and with the same abilities to judge.

He believed that agreements, rather than disagreements, were the destination points in men's intellectual itineraries.

He observed that men spoke gratefully not of their successful disagreements but of their successful agreements, and that they spoke regretfully not of their failures to disagree but of their failures to agree.

He believed that few men would long agree on specific falsehoods, and that more men would agree more lastingly on specific truths.

But Mr. Quattlebaum refrained from jumping to the conclusion that any test of truth which fostered human agreement was therefore a sound test of truth. He was quite aware that men could agree on falsehood, and he was inclined to believe that truth was truth whether men agreed upon it or not.

To define truth—to find its nature, essence, sources and tests—obviously would require a careful look at all of its alleged credentials.

Mr. Quattlebaum could find no honest shortcut.

10. Reason?

Mr. Quattlebaum was inclined—but hesitant—to begin by accepting reason as at least one valid test of truth, as at least one attribute of truth, and as at least one part of the very meaning of truth.

He was so inclined because reason had been in fact, throughout human history, the test of truth most universally employed and most indispensable (or most undispensed with). To reject reason as a test of truth would be to destroy every shred of man's past and present understanding of the universe and to prevent all future understanding. For comprehension by reason was the very meaning of understanding.

Yet he was hesitant because he did not wish, at the very start of his quest for the nature and tests of truth, to beg the very first question to confront him. Might not reason, as we know it, be "still evolving"—and hence somehow still incomplete or immature—and hence an imperfect test of truth? Might there not be "another kind" of man—in future eras or on other planets, for example—somehow empowered to employ a non-thinking "equivalent" of thought, a non-rational "equivalent" of reason? Mr. Quattlebaum was willing to defer judgment. And, later, he would be pleased that he had.

In the meantime, however, it was quite evident to Mr. Quattlebaum that even to ask to examine the credentials of reason as a valid test of truth would be dramatically naïve. For reason, presently if not ultimately, was the credentials committee itself. To employ reason as a test of truth was a part of man's very essence. Man was literally unable to reject reason. He could only pretend to reject it. Actually to reject reason would be to cease to be a man.

And any "argument" against reason as a "valid" test of truth would be itself a resort to the very use of reason which such an argument would seek to reject.

In fact, Mr. Quattlebaum insisted, either reason was a valid test of truth, at least for the present, or man was in the paradoxical position of being unable to make rational evaluation of the credentials of any *other* alleged test of truth.

11. Self-Evidence?

It seemed quite evident to Mr. Quattlebaum that two and two were four.

It seemed equally evident that nothing could both be and not be in the same place at the same time.

Such simple, apparent truths of mathematics and logic seemed in fact *self*-evident—requiring no proof or reasoning—and perhaps self-evident even independently of sensory perception.

But why?

Was it their self-evidence which made them true? Or was their self-evidence no more than a possibly irrelevant by-product of their truth—a truth constituted by other factors and demonstrable only under a more basic criterion? Mr. Quattlebaum preferred to continue his search for more fundamental elements and tests of truth. Later he was to feel that his patience had been rewarded.

In the meantime, however, he felt that he had more than enough reason to conclude that self-evidence was not a dependable test of truth—that truth did not become truth merely by seeming self-evident. For he often observed that what seemed self-evident to one person did not seem self-evident to another, and that what had seemed universally self-evident at one time had been refuted universally at another.

It seemed to him that no appearance or feeling of self-evidence was enough to confirm the truth of anything.

12. Faith?

Although faith might be described poetically as the substance of things hoped for, Mr. Quattlebaum rather promptly concluded that it was not the substance of truth.

He acknowledged that truth warrants faith or belief.

But he insisted that mere faith or belief warrants no conclusion that any thing, event or proposition which is believed is therefore true.

He insisted that nothing is true simply because it is believed, that nothing can be made "truer" by intensifying one's efforts to have faith in it, and that merely to have faith in something can neither constitute, reveal nor confirm its truth.

He observed that men can and often do have faith unwittingly in falsehood—that two men can have equal faith in two propositions which can be shown to be at least partly contradictory, in which instance at least one of the propositions must be at least partly false.

"And why," Mr. Quattlebaum would ask, "does the belief that faith is not a dependable test of truth prevail less universally in 'religious' circles than in 'secular' circles?"

He observed that in offices, fields and factories blind faith was regarded generally, and with intellectual integrity, as a weakness, an imperfection, a danger. When avoidable or wilful, it was criticised as a reckless shortcoming or punished as a "sin."

Yet in many churches it was not always clear whether the disavowals of blind faith outnumbered the instances of its actual encouragement as something somehow desirable, as a mode of perfection, as a source or mark of strength, and indeed as a virtue.

Mr. Quattlebaum could not understand that. He believed that "it is wrong always, everywhere and for anyone, to believe anything upon insufficient evidence."[1]

"O, but you are talking about blind faith," some of his friends would say. "And we are talking about enlightened faith."

Despite his emotional stability, this comment always tended to infuriate Mr. Quattlebaum.

"For god's sake," he would reply, "what is the difference? Blind faith is faith based upon no evidence. Enlightened faith is faith based upon evidence which is valid—but valid not because anyone has faith in it, but for some other reason."

He contended that the truth of any tenet of faith is tested either in the light of no evidence, in which case it is not tested at all, or in the light of "some other reason" than faith, in which case there is no relationship between the truth of a proposition and the amount of faith someone may have in it before its truth is established on some other ground.

To him it seemed well and good to have enlightened faith in, or enlightened faithfulness to, those beliefs which seemed sound. To him it seemed equally well and good to have enlightened doubt, to remain determined not to be faithful to beliefs until indeed they did seem sound.

But he insisted that it was not the faith in "enlightened faith," any more than it was the doubt in "enlightened doubt," that made it tenable. Rather it was the enlightenment itself. And enlightenment was a degree of conviction based upon evidence which pure faith could not contain and could not provide.

Mr. Quattlebaum had concluded that no amount of faith alone could confirm the truth of anything.

13. Authority?

Could anything be true, or become true, or become known to be true, simply because someone said it was true?

Mr. Quattlebaum thought not.

He did not believe that a mere act of assertion, even by an "authority," could constitute truth or be a dependable test of truth.

It was not that he denied the usefulness of reasonably constituted authority. He saw jurisdictional authority as a requisite of family and social composure and progress. He saw specialized intellectual authority as inevitable and invaluable in a world too complex to permit even the most intelligent of men to comprehend more than a tiny fraction of total human knowledge or to push back its frontiers in more than pygmy thrusts. And he acknowledged that religious or moral "authority" could help some persons to foresee important consequences of their actions and to improve their standards of behavior, although he felt it important that such authoritarian "assistance" not mitigate the understanding and sensitivity of which any person might be capable autonomously.

But however proper or useful authority might be, Mr. Quattlebaum did not believe that truth was truth because "authorities" found it, but rather that men became authorities because of the truth which they found.

He believed that men hypothetically accepted such truth not ultimately upon the "authority" of its discoverers or champions, but only in recognition of the probability that it met successfully a basic, valid test of truth—which, he believed, mere "authority" was not.

How, for example, did men distinguish between the agreed-upon and the controversial? Surely, Mr. Quattlebaum reflected, men required and in fact employed a criterion more fundamental than authoritarian admonition, which by definition was too casuistic and non-rational to permit concern with the relevancies of fine circumstance.

He observed that such distinctions were made only by reason and that only reason determined the point, which varied with the man and with the authority, at which healthy respect for healthy authority began—and ended.

It therefore seemed to Mr. Quattlebaum that any man who cited a specific authority as a source or test of truth did so either for a reason, in which case he recognized reason as a test of truth more fundamental than authority, or for no reason at all, in which case his choice was blind or arbitrary.

"For what do we have on our hands," Mr. Quattlebaum mused, "when two 'authorities' disagree? Or when one of their supposedly orthodox disciples disputes a point with another? Or when two beliefs, each held to be true 'on authority,' are found to be in apparent conflict? Must not at least one of them be at least partly in error? For surely truth cannot be in conflict with itself."

And he observed that such "authorities" and authoritarians, in attempts to resolve their differences, must and in fact did begin to argue, discuss and rationalize—and thus to abandon authority as a source and test of truth and to resort instead to reason—if not to force.

Nor was "authority" as a source or test of truth made more plausible for Mr. Quattlebaum by reminders that great numbers of "authorities" had persisted in agreement, or by demonstrations that the assertions of some "authorities" had seemed to survive the centuries. For he knew that majorities could be wrong and minorities right. He believed that truth known for centuries must have been truth before the first "authority" said so. He knew that falsehood, like truth, could long endure. And he knew that much which had been called "true" on yesterday's "authority" was in conflict with today's truth, and that "in all that makes for wisdom we are not younger but older than our ancestors."[1]

But an "authority" great enough to "work miracles"—would not his word be a sufficient source and test of truth? Mr. Quattlebaum observed that the "miraculousness" of such events as the parting of the Red Sea seemed to be dissolving in the testing fluids of Old and New Testament research. He wondered whether "miracles" generally would remain so classified in the light of continued study, and if so in what senses. He also asked whether any necessary relationship could be presumed to exist *ipso facto* between even a "real miracle" and the nature or presence of truth, or even of god.

And upon the word of which "miracle"-working "authority," Mr. Quattlebaum wondered, could men be expected to agree as a dependable test of truth? Would it be a Buddhist "authority"? Or a Christian? Or a Moslem? Or a spokesman of the forces of darkness and evil? Each group claimed its "miracles." Yet the creed of each differed in some respects from the other three. "To work a miracle" was not therefore to become an "authority" whose word was a dependable test of truth. For beliefs of "miracle"-workers were in conflict. And it was not the nature of truth to be in conflict with itself.

Nor could Mr. Quattlebaum agree that the word of an "authority" might be established as a valid criterion of truth merely by summoning "character witnesses" to attest to the greatness, goodness, expertness, "truthfulness" or general prestige of a particular "authority."

He insisted that, however noble an "authority" might be, it was not nobility which assured or constituted truth. A noble "authority" might always intend to speak the truth, but the world was full of honest mistakes. Many men "too honest to lie" had professed their beliefs in all sincerity but also in frequent conflict—which, for Mr. Quattlebaum, was not a sign of truth.

But among his friends there were those who held that, even if human authority must be rejected as a dependable test of truth, divine authority must be accepted not only as one valid test but as the most infallible of all tests of truth. How could one dispute the truth of anything discovered through access to divine omniscience? Might not such access in fact remove the need of any further test at all? Divine truth, perfect and self-revealed, would seem to carry its own sanction.

"But tests of truth are not for the omniscient," Mr. Quattlebaum replied, "or for those with special access to omniscient sources. They are for men. And any man's judgment that a particular 'authority' is divine can be itself no more than a merely human judgment. This is why men do not and cannot yet agree upon which if any specific 'authority' is in fact 'divine,' or even upon a meaning of 'divine' itself."

And even if it were now possible for men to agree upon a specific "divine authority," Mr. Quattlebaum asked, could they confidently equate its presumably infallible *transmission* of infallible truth with their own merely human *reception* of merely human message data, through merely human receivers, in merely human language?

Might not a single truth transmitted from an omniscient god become ten thousand messages in the minds of ten thousand non-omniscient men?

No man, Mr. Quattlebaum concluded, can point to what he knows god "means," but only to what he believes he heard god say.

The fact that some of his progressive Roman Catholic friends did not take issue with him on this point came at first as a surprise to Mr. Quattlebaum.

He acknowledged that, if they held their church to be an "authority" whose official judgment in the area of faith and morals was free from error, no man could prove them wrong. But he was surprised by their own acknowledgment that no man could prove them right. And he was further surprised by their admission that the world as a whole might be as free from error as they held their church to be.

Mr. Quattlebaum happily agreed with them that a complete, divine truth (whatever that might mean)—safeguarded in a complete, divine context by a divine holy spirit (whatever that might mean)—could indeed be conceived as countenancing or even as mandating that men should view some truth as error, and some error as truth, within their human, fragmentary contexts of incomplete evolution. For these were the only contexts, they agreed, in which men had experience.

They could see that to men within one such context the beliefs of Ptolemy would appear "true," and that to men within another such context the "truths" of Copernicus would appear to make "errors" of the "truths" of Ptolemy.

And they also could see that to a god—in a complete, divine context of complete, divine truth (whatever that might mean)— both the Ptolemaic and Copernican assertions might appear as errors, or both might appear as truth. To such a god, in such a context, both the Ptolemaic and Copernican theses might in fact appear as "ultimate error" which man, nevertheless—by virtue of his very predicament in two human, fragmentary contexts of his evolution—might be forced to embrace as "necessary truth."

Even if men should catch glimpses of "divine truth," they agreed that it might not and possibly could not "mean" to men what it might "mean" to god.

It was therefore at least conceivable to them that a holy spirit (whatever that might mean) could protect from "error" a church which in one fragmentary context could see usury in deliberate conflict with the "natural law" and therefore sinful, and which in another fragmentary context could pay the interest on its building loans and be generally at ease in a credit economy.

They agreed that what men meant by usury at one time, and by a modest finance charge at another, could be two different things. And that what men meant by "natural law" could differ from time to time and from human mind to human mind, however unchanging its "meaning" might be imagined to remain in a divine mind of which men had no certain knowledge.

With the possible exception of the mystic, whose contentions Mr. Quattlebaum had not yet examined, he and his friends agreed that men simply could not know that they "meant" what a god might "mean." Human meanings were the only meanings existentially meaningful to men. Surely, therefore, men could not accept, as a valid test of truth for men, an allegedly "divine authority" whose ultimate "meanings" they could not be sure they even began to comprehend.

"And this," observed one of his Roman Catholic friends, "is why we can believe that our church is in some sense a repository of religious truth without also believing what in fact we cannot believe: that any specific member of the church, or all of its members combined, can comprehend such truth in its entirety. Even a divine commission to 'guard the box' of total truth could not enable its human guardians to comprehend all—or perhaps even much—that the box might contain.

"And this," the friend continued, "is why fewer and fewer holds are barred as the left and right wings of theology and church journalism broaden their battles over human meanings and rationales of doctrines heretofore presumed, loosely and without definition, to be 'divinely inspired.' Billions of still invisible implications of religious doctrine, including the fundamental nature of the church itself, have yet to evolve, yet to be discovered, yet to be examined, yet to be rejected or agreed upon by men."

Mr. Quattlebaum began to suspect that what Roman Catholics referred to as an assurance from their church—that it was not "authority" but rather an informed conscience, a voice of reason, which was their ultimate test of truth—might be less a token assurance, and more a fundamental assurance, than he had realized.

He began to feel that no responsible Roman Catholic ever again would contend that "if the formulas of modern science contradict the science of Catholic dogma, it is the former that must be altered, not the latter."[2]

He hoped that in the future there would be less need of such observations as the one for which he felt so grateful to Coleridge: "He who begins by loving Christianity better than truth will proceed by loving his own sect or Church better than Christianity, and end in loving himself better than all."[3]

He hoped, too, that he would be confronted increasingly by articles like the one, by a non-Catholic professor of religion, which he had read in a magazine edited by Catholics:

"If a Catholic has a problem, the answer he gets depends on whom he asks . . . I would like . . . to know *the* Catholic teaching . . . but . . . different tutors tell me different things . . . it gives me great heart and hope, for it indicates clearly . . . that there is not one way, and one way only, to define the faith . . . if I wanted the kind of theological *securitas* that typical Catholic apologetics claim that Mother Church provides . . . I would not become a Roman Catholic but a Southern Baptist . . . a reasonably well-read Catholic . . . is not simply presented with *the* answer. He is confronted with a variety of ways of interpreting . . . doctrine and finally he must, in the interior of his own heart, make his own act of assent. Nobody else can make it for him, and though the church and his spiritual directors can help him . . . finally the decision is his. And, as Catholic theology has long taught, he must make it in conformity with . . . his own conscience. He cannot pretend to believe what . . . he finds it impossible to believe. Even though his conscience be objectively in error, its subjective integrity must be honored . . . I find the situation of the Catholic to be much closer to the situation of the Protestant than I used to imagine it to be."[4]

It was not a matter of compromise. Mr. Quattlebaum was happy to see religion becoming more rational. But, as a rational man, he still could not acknowledge "authority" as a valid test of truth.

He knew that "authorities" could be invaluable. Some were a rich and often unique source of concepts which could become deeply meaningful to men in meditation. But how could meditation be meditation, he asked, unless it were rational?

Reason was a test of truth which he observed that men in their very nature must apply, which they could not avoid applying, and which they could only pretend not to apply.

But *argumentum ad hominem* was a fallacy.
Mere "authority" was not a dependable test of truth.

14. Pragmatism?

Mr. Quattlebaum's rejection of the pragmatic as a test of truth was neither swift nor smug.

For a time he found pragmatism appealingly plausible.

He liked its emphasis upon "results" and practicality, and upon the worth and importance of individual judgment.

He liked the apparent honesty of its disdain of abstract intangibles.

He liked its respect for the here and now.

Why, then, did he conclude that not even the pragmatist could believe that pragmatism could offer a valid test of truth?

The pragmatist, Mr. Quattlebaum explained, believed that any belief which "worked" (by satisfying any desire or presumed need of any person who happened to hold such a belief) was automatically a "true" belief for that particular person—and one which that person had an automatic "moral right" to hold. The pragmatist, he observed, said that you might and should believe what was "true for you" (your "true belief"), and that I might and should believe what was "true for me" (my "true belief").

But please note, Mr. Quattlebaum went on, that while the pragmatist believed in beliefs he did not believe in "truth."

Pragmatism could not be a test of truth because pragmatism did not believe that there was any truth to test.

Actually, Mr. Quattlebaum added, pragmatism was in fact a wholesale denial of every man's right to seek truth at all—because it was a sweepingly arbitrary denial that there was any truth to seek.

It was an empty generosity with which the pragmatist proclaimed every man's right to believe whatever it pleased him to believe; for pragmatism contended that, whatever any man might decide to believe, there wouldn't be a word of "truth" in it.

In a note to a pragmatist friend, Mr. Quattlebaum wrote:

"I have been doing some interesting reading. I look forward to your reactions to a few marked passages when next we meet. Meanwhile they prompt the following observations and questions:

"You say that a thousand logically conflicting beliefs about god, held by a thousand equally satisfied persons, are equally 'true.' But don't you really mean that you hold their mere *beliefs* to be in some sense 'true'? For you long have denied in effect that there is or can be any truth in *what* they believe.

"As you watch a thousand persons using their 'freedom' to embrace a thousand different beliefs about god, you as a pragmatist may be confident that they may learn much about their beliefs. But must you not be equally confident that they can learn nothing at all about god?[1]

"Why do I believe that you have backed yourself into this corner?

"Simply because it seems clear to me that *'no* assertion can have any meaning' for the pragmatist. 'If it had a meaning it would not mean that meaning, but (only) something about the belief in that meaning.'[2]

"As a pragmatist you insist that there is no such thing as a useless truth. You say it is not 'true' that two and two are four, or that Japan is an island, unless and until it satisfies your—or someone's—personal need or desire to believe so. And you say in effect that nothing can be 'false'—neither the fiveness of two and two, nor the peninsularity of Japan, nor the Pope's presidency of B'nai B'rith—if it is satisfying or useful to someone to pretend that such 'falsehood' is 'true.' Actually, are you not saying that a perfect liar's lie is 'true' for anyone for whom it 'works'?[3] (I am sure that you would reply that, in using the word 'liar,' I am begging the whole question. So I shall return to that point in a moment.)

"But let me first say that I respect your consistency in acknowledging in your recent letter that you as a pragmatist deny that there is any objective truth in history. As you might guess, I do not agree that historical events have ceased to 'work.' I am not even sure that I can agree that past events are no longer in some sense present to satisfy current desires or needs. But I do agree that as a pragmatist you remain consistent when you say that every man is free to deny history altogether—or to write his own.

"However, as you go about selecting your historical 'truths' as one might pick grapes, I trust you will be tolerant of my own surmise that some of your grapes may be in fact artificial or imaginary. Will you, for example, 'pick' the historical 'truth' that Hitler was a benevolent influence? Or that such a person never lived? Or that only irrelevancies were spoken by Martin Luther or by Martin Luther King?

"As a pragmatist you now say that each man is free to choose his own beliefs, and that there is 'truth' only in those which satisfy his own desires or needs or which 'work' by jibing with preconceptions which bring him pleasant satisfaction.

"But I respectfully predict that you yourself eventually will come to acknowledge this as the very heart of the 'central trouble' with pragmatism:

" 'When we *choose* our belief, it ceases to be our *belief!*'[4]

"A man may 'choose' to believe that he owns a trillion dollars," Mr. Quattlebaum's letter continued. "But it seems to me that his intellectual integrity and mental health would be less in jeopardy if he were to believe the fifty-dollar figure in his savings book and thus remain communicative with a society for which 'to believe' means to believe *something*. By 'belief' rational men simply do not mean a merely expedient or personally satisfying experience. By 'belief' they mean the mind's valid or invalid assent to an objective 'truth.'

"But what, you may demand, is an objective 'truth'? It is a fair question—and one, as you know, to which I still seek an answer. If you were to 'argue' that I have no right to over-bandy the term until I can define it, I would readily agree. I do not wish to argue in a circle or to beg any question.

"But I must remind you that as a pragmatist you have no right to argue at all—with me or with anyone else—at any time—about anything. The pragmatist may find it pleasantly satisfying or expedient to pretend a disbelief in the laws of reason. But when he 'argues' against their objectivity, he uses those very laws of reason in an appeal to the validity of the very 'truth' he 'argues' against.

"If there are no laws of reason with which I can prove your pragmatism wrong, there are certainly no laws of reason with which you can prove your pragmatism right—or anything else wrong.

"If the laws of reason are a valid test of truth, pragmatism is wrong. If the laws of reason are not an objective 'truth,' then *no* 'truth' is meaningful. Meaning itself becomes meaningless. And all of man's painfully won 'knowledge' disintegrates into one inscrutably vast and ghastly chaos.

"By denying that 'truth' is objective, when 'something objective' is what society *means* by 'truth,' you as a pragmatist pretend to *leave* society. But to 'pretend' is the best you can do. You cannot really leave society because you are unavoidably one of the rational men of whom society is comprised."

It seemed to Mr. Quattlebaum that pragmatists never really succeeded in their efforts to deny objective truth. Rather they seemed merely to struggle to ignore indications of its possibility. For to him they seemed interested, as he had observed, not in 'truth' at all, but only in 'beliefs' which satisfied them.

He thought it sadly paradoxical that pragmatists, in disputing the possibility of objective 'truth,' cut themselves off from the possible satisfaction of possibly knowing why their satisfactions were satisfying. In regarding satisfying consequences of satisfying beliefs as their only standard of truth, pragmatists seemed needlessly to abandon all opportunity to discover whether such consequences really constituted the only standard of truth—or whether they were mere corollaries of another standard which they never chose to seek.

Mr. Quattlebaum rejected the pragmatic as a test of truth because it seemed clear to him that pragmatism was a wholly arbitrary denial that there was any truth to test.

To him it seemed an irrational denial that men were rational— by rational men who could only pretend that they were not.

15. Intuition?

Yes, Mr. Quattlebaum acknowledged, there were some persons—including his good wife—who had a seemingly uncanny "talent" for hunches or premonitions, for quick apprehensions or instinctive convictions, which quite often proved to be correct.

But could the content of such intuitions, or the "talent" for such intuitional experience, provide a dependable test of truth?

Mr. Quattlebaum thought not.

He observed that two or more intuitions could and often did yield conflicting conclusions, at least one of which must be at least partly false—because "truth" in conflict with itself was not what men meant by truth.

The "truth" in a "true" intuition was not recognized as true simply because it was intuited, he insisted, but rather because it successfully met the more fundamental test of reason or "fact." A hunch that Daddy Longlegs would win the Kentucky Derby could not be recognized as a "true" hunch until in fact that horse had won that race. Nor was the uncanniness of a man's "talent" for true intuitions attributable to the mere frequency of such experiences, but rather to the frequency with which they were "proved true" in the light of reason or "fact." (Mr. Quattlebaum was aware that he had not yet defined "fact," but the definition at which he would later arrive would seem to him to confirm rather than to weaken the point which he was trying to make here.)

"Actually," Mr. Quattlebaum remarked to a friend one evening, "I have begun to suspect that even the very essence of intuition may not be the non-rational phenomenon which most of us have presumed it to be.

"I grant you that it is supposed to be generally characteristic of intuition to seem wholly independent of reason. I grant you that the person who has a hunch, premonition, quick apprehension or instinctive conviction experiences an awareness which seems immediate and direct.

"I further grant you," he went on, "that such a person usually cannot explain how or why the intuition occurs, and that he is not aware of any step-by-step process of reasoning from premises to conclusion.

"And yet," Mr. Quattlebaum noted, "there do seem to be indications that intuition may be a sort of 'intellectual shorthand' in which one rational step follows another, but too swiftly to permit human awareness of an intricate pattern which may be present."

What he had in mind was the fact that many intuitions which "proved true" seemed to follow relevant experience. They seemed to occur upon a base of already existing knowledge.

"I wonder, for example," he said, "whether an admiral's intuitions could really reveal anything beyond the previously unexpressed implications latent within the context of his naval and other knowledge and experience. A mathematician suddenly may grasp previously elusive relationships within a mathematical hypothesis. An architect on a fishing trip may have an unexpected 'vision' of how to enlarge corridors in plans for a new school without increasing costs.

"But does the average stenographer ever intuit revolutionary formulas for interplanetary fuels?"

Increasingly Mr. Quattlebaum became intrigued by the notion that intuitional "conclusions" might be preceded by a humanly invisible process of rapid, rational deduction from familiar premises. He felt that an intuition might be "a vision of an integrated whole of parts,"[1] or at least a cluster of parts somehow related—whether aided by sensory perception, as in a chess game, or with less or no use of the senses, as in the grasping of a mathematical proof.

But in either event, whether intuitions were the result of essentially rational activity or not, Mr. Quattlebaum felt that they could not constitute a dependable test of truth.

While they could and did yield truth, they also could and did yield error.

And, with the possible exception of the allegedly "mystic" experience, concerning which he had not yet formulated his views, it seemed to him clear that the degree of truth or error yielded by an intuition could be determined reliably only by resort to a test of truth more fundamental than that of intuition itself.

16. Mysticism?

It promised to be quite an evening.

Would "Quattlebaum the rationalist" endorse mysticism as a valid source or test of truth?

Clare Proffitt and Dr. Reasner, the two friends whom he had asked over for beer and pretzels, knew that he could not accept conventional intuition as a source or test of truth.

But what about "the *big* intuition"—the mystic experience?

They had heard him remark that "most of the arguments against mysticism aren't worth a damn." He had not elaborated. But it was the only thing on tonight's agenda, and they were looking forward to it.

They began by agreeing upon definition. Each acknowledged that the alleged mystic experience connoted a vast, direct and inerrant intuitional insight into the fundamental nature of reality, and even into the very nature of god. They further agreed that it was said to resemble conventional intuition in that the mystic was unaware of any step-by-step reasoning process, but to differ from ordinary intuition in that the awed and overwhelmed mystic could not express the wonders which he was said to behold.

"The mystic also is generally supposed to be in a state of emotional ecstasy," Mr. Proffitt added. "And this is not surprising because he is convinced that he sees and knows and literally identifies with a fundamental 'truth' which is somehow single, complete, unified and all-good—but which he is powerless to describe to his fellow men in more than fragments. An 'insider's' mystic experience is thus discouragingly difficult, and in most or all respects quite impossible, for an 'outsider' to assess."

"Yes," Dr. Reasner partially agreed, "but by that very token no responsible *non*-mystic has any right to assert the validity or even the existence of truth-revealing, truth-constituting or dependably truth-testing 'mystic experiences.' "

"But he does have a right," Mr. Quattlebaum broke in, "and even an intellectual obligation, to cite fallacies in those arguments which commonly purport to demonstrate or suggest that such experiences *cannot* exist."

Clare Proffitt. Absolutely. For example, Doc might argue that a mystic's mere feeling of certainty is not enough to confirm or to constitute truth—that one may feel profoundly convinced and still be profoundly wrong. I would agree. So would you, Quat. But surely, Doc, reason requires us to acknowledge that the "truth" about which the mystic feels so certain could be true for reasons other than his feeling of certainty—reasons beyond the non-mystic's power to imagine or to conceive, reasons apparent only within a context which the non-mystic has not experienced, reasons beyond the mystic's own ability to explain.

Dr. Reasner. Truth without reason? Isn't that meaningless? To speak of mystic "truth" outside a context of reason—isn't that to speak of nothing at all? For me, at least, "truth" allegedly revealed in an indescribable mystic experience is simply not imaginable.

Mr. Quattlebaum. Why not? I agree that a mystic experience cannot be rationalized because it cannot be described. But it doesn't follow that the content of an alleged mystic experience need be fundamentally irrational or non-rational. It is simply inaccessible. It cannot be examined. And so the non-mystic cannot know whether it is rationally structured or not.

Prof. I have to agree with Quat on that. Listen to this from

William James. "If you were to tell a man who was himself without experience (of the phenomenon of sleep) that there are people who at times swoon away so as to resemble dead men, and who (in dreams) yet perceive things that are hidden, he would deny it (and give his reasons). Nevertheless, his arguments would be refuted by actual experience."[1] I'm sure you've had dreams, Doc. And I'm sure you know more than I about increasingly successful efforts to study their hypothetical rationale. How, then, can you say that you can't even *conceive* of mystic experiences? How can you say that their content *cannot* be rational fundamentally, even if not yet demonstrably?

Reas. Touché. But a mere ability to imagine a mystic experience does not compel one to regard it as a valid source or test of truth. The content of some alleged mystic experiences has been contradicted by the content of others. The content of some has been contradicted by propositions universally acknowledged to be true. I contend that alleged mystic experiences—like self-evidence, faith, authority, pragmatism and common intuition—do not constitute a dependable source or test of truth because they can and do assert rationally incompatible propositions—not all of which can be true because, as you yourself have said so often, Quat, truth cannot be in conflict with itself.

Quat. You quote me correctly but out of context. If it is characteristic of the alleged mystic experience to be indescribable and thus incommunicable, the content of two or more such experiences obviously cannot be compared or contrasted at all—by you, by me, by any other non-mystic, or even by mystics themselves. And surely what cannot be compared or contrasted cannot be held to be in conflict. It seems to me that only an omniscient mind, comprehending the intuitions of hundreds of mystics, could know them to be in conflict. Yet I can conceive that an omniscient mind might find them all compatible—and all true.

Reas. Can you also conceive that an omniscient mind might find compatibility and truth in the thousands of similar and equally bizarre experiences which can be induced by drugs?

Quat. As a physician you know much more than I about the

content of drug-induced experiences. But the three of us have agreed that, as non-mystics, we can know nothing about the content of alleged mystic experiences. So I must insist that you cannot know whether alleged mystic experiences are really "bizarre," or therefore whether they and drug-induced experiences are "equally bizarre," or even whether they are "similar" in any respect or degree at all.

Prof. And even if such similarity were to be established, where is the evidence that truth cannot be revealed in an experience induced by drugs? Don't "truth serums" often induce evidence which subsequent reasoning finds to contain more truth than does some evidence which is not drug-induced? Isn't truth truth, whatever its proximate source? One can "see the light" while robbing a bank, practicing prostitution or taking drugs.

Reas. But wouldn't you say that the nature of the "light" which a person may "see" is determined by the nature of that person's particular pre-conditioning? Let me read you something which suggests to me that mystics, for example, experience what they have been intellectually or psychologically pre-conditioned to experience. It suggests that variations in their alleged mystic experiences may be, paralleled by variations in their prior beliefs or in their frames of mind. "For the Hindu, the (mystic) experience means oneness with Brahma, for the Christian it is union with Christ . . . for an agnostic like Richard Jefferies, it is a oneness with the ineffable beauty of Nature."[2] Now how can three conflicting mystics profess three conflicting "onenesses" with three conflicting sets of beliefs—and still confront each other with an expressed conviction that each has been face-to-face with the *one* fundamental nature of reality?

Prof. Again you fail to acknowledge that, as a non-mystic, you are in no position to know whether the reported "onenesses" are in conflict, or whether mystic experience really reflects the pre-conditioning of the mystic. If the experience is ineffable, only the mystic can know what it contains. He is powerless to report which if any pre-conditioning the experience may have reflected.

Reas. But it is not I—it is the mystic himself who has referred to his experience in terms of Brahma, Jesus or Richard Jefferies.

Prof. Yes, but he has done so not during but after the experience —when he is admittedly powerless to describe it.

Reas. You seem to be giving the mystic his cake and letting him eat it, too. If his experience is indescribable, Clare, why does he try to describe it?

Prof. The desire to share startling experiences is universal. The greater the experience, the greater the desire to share—even if such a sharing is impossible, as mystics universally declare it to be. The mystic's desire and attempt to share what he himself says cannot be shared is admittedly inconsistent. But it is equally innocent and beside the point. The point is, Doc, that none of us has any right to equate the allegedly indescribable with the product of a frustrated attempt to describe.

Reas. But isn't it possible that a mystic's experience really does parallel his pre-conditioning in terms of a Brahma or a Jesus or a Richard Jefferies?

Prof. I would even say probable. But now it's you who want to have your cake and eat it. If I were to admit that an experience could not be genuinely mystic unless it were the experience of a person who was not psychologically or intellectually pre-conditioned in one way or another, I would lose the argument by default. For surely no such person exists. How could a man be a man and not be somehow pre-conditioned? What is life itself if not a conditioning? And, as non-mystics, can you and I know that two alleged mystic experiences—one by a Jesus-conditioned mystic, and one by a Jefferies-conditioned mystic—cannot include insights into the selfsame truth? If mystics are given insight into a truth which is complete and unified, could we not intelligently expect it to be a truth in which "limited particulars" are somehow embraced within a "limitless universal"?

Reas. I wouldn't know, Clare. You lose me when you get into phrases like "limitless visions by limited men." Hell, I don't know much about *this* world. So how can I pontificate on a world beyond? Give me a few hundred years to understand the complexities of the natural, the physical, the profane. Maybe then I'll be ready to think about divinity and the supernatural and all that.

Quat. How do you know there's any difference?

Reas. I don't.

Quat. I don't, either. It seems to me that everyone just assumes that the "divine" or the "supernatural" is something essentially separate and necessarily removed from men and from "this world." Perhaps this is the world's most dramatic example of how to beg the big question—of how to reason one's way to magnificent conclusions without first putting one's humble premises to the test of truth or fact.

Reas. Frankly, Quat, that's why I don't go to church. I'm just not an easy believer. I can't pretend to be irrational about religious notions which millions of men have treasured through the centuries, but which to me and to other millions seem naïve. I agree with you that a fundamental separateness of the natural and the supernatural may be no more than a gratuitous assumption.

Prof. But isn't the hardback sceptic equally presumptuous? Does he have any more right to reject a notion of a supernatural than your "easy believer" has to accept it?

Quat. Ironic, isn't it? One group seems too quick to accept, and another group seems too quick to reject, a supernatural which neither has carefully examined.

Reas. It seems to me that some easy believers are quick to embrace mysticism because they so love whatever smacks of the excitingly mysterious or miraculous. They like to believe or hope that the supernatural, which the mystic is said to perceive, is almost inaccessible—but not quite. If it resides in a space beyond space, or in a fourth dimension, or on a jeweled throne in a gold-paved heaven, so much the better—because men's alleged mystic experiences of it can thus be heralded as religious victories all the more dramatic.

Prof. Some feel that way, Doc, but not all. Perhaps the sceptic too quickly rejects mysticism because he unwarrantedly assumes that the supernatural, which the mystic is said to perceive, must mean what your easy believer says it means. And I sympathize with your reluctance to accept such irrational potpourri. But suppose there really is some truth in the murky water which men, too loosely and with too much vestigial superstition, call supernatural.

Might not the sceptic's too-hasty rejection (of what he has not bothered to examine) amount to throwing out the baby with the bath?

Reas. Perhaps. I just don't know.

Quat. I agree that the sceptic may be criticized for rejecting what he has not examined. But to me the easy believer seems the guiltier of the two. He has a longstanding reputation for a pretended and uncontrite irrationality. And this leaves the sceptic with the unfortunate impression that it is essentially characteristic of religion to dispense itself from the disciplines of reason—which I would deny. But, wherever the fault may lie, the fact remains that many of men's notions of the supernatural are garbled—too garbled to permit clear resolution of some of the disputes over the validity of men's allegedly mystic experience of "supernatural truth."

Reas. Yes, something is wrong when easy believers appear to resent every humble effort to understand their "limitless supernatural," and when they seem to fear that increased understanding of it would render it somehow less "sacred." I wonder why such persons line our highways with signs admonishing men to "get close to god." Normally one does not move close by remaining as far away as possible.

Prof. No, but something else is wrong when sceptics listen to an easy believer's wild description of a "limitless supernatural," and then jump to the conclusion that *no* "limitless supernatural" can be mystically experienced by "limited" or "psychologically conditioned" men—as if there could be any other kind of man.

Reas. May I move on to another point? Alleged mystics seem to agree that the "ultimate reality" into which they are assumed to peer is both complete and completely good. How can it be complete and still omit the evil which is apparent to all men, even to mystics themselves between mystic experiences?

Prof. Perhaps evil is apparent only in partial contexts. A boy views a spanking as evil. As a man he may look back upon the spanking as a good. The later judgment is better informed, less naïve and more mature. I can therefore conceive that what appears evil in partial contexts might appear good in the "total context" which is said to characterize the mystic experience.

Reas. Would you employ the same logic to explain the mystic's belief that pain and matter are unreal and illusory?

Prof. Somewhat, yes.

Reas. I prefer the logic of those who argue that a Christian Scientist or a Hindu cannot rationally seek to alleviate pain if pain is only illusory.[3]

Prof. All of us experience illusions. Why is it irrational to try to rid oneself of them? Such efforts are in fact generally commended. Perhaps it is not pain as a fundamental reality, but rather the cause of pain's seeming to be real, which Christian Scientists, Hindus and many others seek to alleviate—apparently with striking success. And, although Christian Scientists, ascetics, mystics and many rationalists may doubt the ultimate reality of matter as such, they do not foolishly deny the existence of those "material objects" which all men experience. Nor do they generally regard "matter" as inherently evil.[4] They merely regard it as something necessarily less than the supreme good or complete truth which they believe can be conceived only within a complete context. They may see matter as something which, if presumed actually to be what they believe it only appears to be, would not merely hamper mystic concentration but perhaps also stiflingly confine all of men's rational efforts within an area of mere naïveté. But to pursue this latter point would get us off our immediate subject.

Reas. That might be a good idea. I see no point in any further laboring of the alleged mystic experience. Even if there is such a thing, what value can it have for mankind as a whole? If no mystic can communicate its content to others—if it cannot yield new general knowledge with which to supplement existing knowledge or hypotheses—if it cannot facilitate men's efforts to solve the problems of the world—why waste time on it? Why not admit that the alleged mystic experience can give mankind no more truth than do intermittent dreams? Why not place both in the category of relative uselessness?

Prof. It is not that simple. It is the very nature of man, and at least a part of his apparent role, to seek and nurture truth and to safeguard its sources and its tests. Responsible men will not arbitrarily cut themselves off from any possible source of truth until they are certain that it cannot be a valid and dependable source. Despite its relative inaccessibility, the mystic experience has not yet been proved to be an invalid or undependable source of truth. It is not yet even understood. Who can presume to assess its potential?

Quat. For that matter, who can presume to assess even the present value to mankind of the alleged mystic himself? Who can know that whatever experience he may have cannot make him more valuable to mankind than he would be without such experience? I am persuaded that not every alleged mystic has been the hypercredulous, reason-shunning prototype which the word so often suggests. Many have been loyal servants of reason, inclined and determined to make conscientiously careful studies of every remnant of their experiences. Many have seemed as disheartened as any non-mystic to find such remnants so discouragingly few. As if with batteries recharged by their experiences, and possibly with residual insights into how the pieces of the universe might fit together in a meaningful whole, many alleged mystics have turned by choice and with impressive resolve to a new quest of non-mystic truth, exclusively within the area of conscious, step-by-step reason.[5]

Reas. Interesting and encouraging. But may I assume that it does not lead you to minimize the fact that the so-called mystic experience does remain indescribable and thus loses at least much of its significance in the course of efforts to explain it by "building it in" with the rest of the mystic's knowledge?

Quat. Of course. And yet one might harmlessly observe that many acknowledged truths from non-mystic sources—equally indescribable by and to some men, and sustaining comparable dilutions of significance in the course of efforts to "build them in" with such persons' other knowledge—are nonetheless true.

Prof. And I'd like to note, before I leave, that I am still impressed by the fact that hundreds of case histories convinced William James, as they have convinced others since, that what he called mystical states were not merely interruptive, that they did modify the inner life between occurrences, that they did "hold up" in the judgment of mystics when they returned to their "normal" environments, and that they did indeed cohere with those environments while mere dreams did not.[6]

Quat. Well, men, have we reached any areas of agreement? Would you agree, for example, that we cannot prove that one may *not* have experiences in which one "recovers the forgotten subject of one's predicates"[7] (or discovers their previously unknown subject)? Would you agree that we cannot prove that one may *not* be confronted by truth in a mystic experience? Would you agree that such truth, if it does exist, is largely indescribable by the alleged mystic to his fellow men? And would you agree that it is at least possible, nevertheless, that those who may have such experiences may be enabled thereby to make enhanced contributions to men's general quest of truth?

Prof. I agree.

Reas. Your conclusions are so elaborately qualified that I can concur without strain. But would you also agree that the non-mystic is not privileged either to share in or to be given a description of a mystic experience, and therefore that such experience can provide neither a source nor a dependable test of truth for any of those non-mystics who seem to constitute the bulk of mankind?

Prof. I agree.

Quat. So do I. We non-mystics cannot know whether the so-called mystic experience can bring truth to the mystic, or whether it can offer him a dependable test of truth. But for us, as non-mystics, the alleged mystic experience can be neither a source nor a dependable test of truth. For we cannot share directly in such experience, and the mystic cannot describe it to us.

Reas. Good enough. Thanks for the beer.

Prof. And the pretzels.

17. Correspondence?

He tossed and turned all night.

Like everyone else, he always had assumed that when he saw a tree he saw a tree.

He always had assumed, when he perceived a tree, that his perception was caused by, and "corresponded" with, a "real" tree.

He always had assumed that such "correspondence" (between a "concrete" object and a sensory perception of that object) was in fact one of man's most dependable and most-depended-upon tests of truth.

And now here he was in the bathroom, shaving for work after a sleepless night, all but convinced that such "correspondence" could not be a dependable test of truth because *such "correspondence" never occurs.*

Mr. Quattlebaum had gone to bed early, content and nicely sleepy. His last thoughts, before the disquieting analysis began, had been of the sassafras trees at his little farm.

And then:

"What really happens when I look at one of these trees? I have perceptions. I perceive. But what do I perceive? Hmmm. I seem to perceive only my perceptions. But that's a tautology. But damned if it doesn't also seem to be a fact. When I perceive a tree, I consciously experience a perception of a tree. I certainly do not consciously experience a 'real' tree which I do not consciously experience. It would be absurd to say that I consciously experience what I do not consciously experience. Therefore I cannot be aware of any 'correspondence' between what I consciously experience and what I do not consciously experience. I cannot fit or match what I experience to what I do not experience."

He had gone to the bathroom for a cigarette.

Surely, he had thought, if a man had a perception of a tree, there must have been a "real" tree to cause the perception.

But why?

"And is it really true that my perception, if caused, must resemble its cause? And, even if it must, how can I ever know whether it actually does—if I can't perceive beyond my perception? Better get some sleep."

Back to bed. More tossing and turning. Sudden memories of college days and the track team. The starting gun. Two perceptions: a loud explosion and a puff of smoke. When had the gun "really" been fired? When he had heard the noise? When he had seen the smoke? Surely the "real" firing of the gun had not been both a single firing and a double firing. Surely it had not been a single firing at two times in two places. Yet two perceptions. Big crowd. Maybe a thousand perceptions. Still only one firing. No "correspondence."

More sassafras trees. "I look at the tree. I experience a perception of the tree. I squint. I experience a perception of two sassafras trees. Does the second perception reveal two 'real' sassafras trees? No 'correspondence.'

"It's too hot in here. I've kicked off the covers four times. Why does Gertrude keep putting them back on? The room's too hot. She must think it's too cold. Is this one room or two? Can a single area be occupied at a single time by two 'real' rooms, one 'too hot' and one 'too cold'? Certainly not. Only one room. Two perceptions. No 'correspondence.'

"Damned mosquitoes! What if they bit eyeballs? How would sassafras trees look through swollen eyes? Without sense organs I couldn't perceive. They tell me what's 'out there.' But swollen eyes could change my perceptions to some extent. To that extent a perception could not 'correspond' with a 'concrete' sassafras tree existing independently of my eyes. If to any extent a sensory perception helps to produce its object, to that extent it cannot reveal that object as it 'really is' before or after the perception. No 'correspondence.' "

Back to the bathroom. Another cigarette.

"Now get hold of yourself, Quattlebaum. You are a man of perhaps average intelligence. You've been living with conflicting sensory perceptions all your life. How have you dealt with them in the past?

"Why of course. You have used that average intelligence to 'compensate' for inaccuracies in your perceptions. You have 'corrected' them by reason—just as you have 'corrected' your memory perceptions (you no longer *really* conduct the kindergarten band). And just as you have 'corrected' your dream perceptions (you are not yet *really* President of the United States). And just as you have 'corrected' your nightmare perceptions (you were not *really* being chased by tigers)."

He crawled back into bed at dawn—and nearly fell asleep.

"But what actually happens," he suddenly wondered, "when we rationally 'correct' a perception? We discard it. What remains is a refined judgment. We no longer even care whether the original perception 'corresponded' with a 'concrete' object.

"Why?

"Because perhaps we have then found what we were really looking for: not a 'concrete' object, but a rationally confirmed conclusion.

"At no point in the whole process do we ever encounter a 'concrete' object at all. And certainly we cannot compare any perception, accurate or inaccurate, with any 'concrete' object which we never encounter.

"In the absence of two things which can be compared, 'correspondence' cannot exist.

"And something which does not exist certainly cannot be a test of truth."

He was very tired. He closed his eyes. His breathing began to deepen. And the alarm clock went off.

Mr. Quattlebaum had come face-to-face with what seemed a shocking probability that men never really experience hard, physical, concrete objects "out there in space and time."

He could not permit an apparent probability to become a revolutionary conviction in just one sleepless night.

But the implications of such a possibility were so far-reaching that he felt an immediate obligation to scrutinize every possible shred of relevant evidence in the weeks ahead.

III

18. Mr. Quattlebaum Looks at His Sassafras Trees

"This is a hell of a note," thought Mr. Quattlebaum as he drove toward his little farm for an afternoon alone.

"If men never really experience hard, physical, concrete objects 'out there in time and space,' then how can truth itself be an 'object'? Is there no such thing as 'objective' truth?"

He had concluded earlier that truth was not subjective in the pragmatist's sense. He had concluded that nothing could be "true for one person" merely because that person found it pleasant to believe, and that nothing could be "false for one person" merely because its denial seemingly "worked" to that person's advantage. He had concluded that by truth society simply did not *mean* the pragmatically subjective, but rather "something objective."

"Yet how can truth be objective," he asked himself, "if subjective consciousness is man's only confirmable source of truth—and truth's only confirmable 'setting' or 'locale'?"

One dilemma followed another.

"Surely consciousness alone cannot be a sufficient, dependable test of truth," he thought as he drove along, "because one can be as conscious of error as of truth. Yet one obviously cannot consciously test an alleged truth of which he is not conscious.

"Then how in heaven's name," he wondered, "can a truth be objective in the sense that it is true independently of any particular person's awareness or acknowledgment of it, and still be subjective in the sense that nothing can be known or held by any man to be objectively true except in his own subjective consciousness?"

Mr. Quattlebaum began to wonder whether he had too quickly rejected a physical, material world of things and events existing "out there in time and space."

It certainly *seemed* that they existed "out there"—not only when he was conscious of them, but also when he was not conscious of them. Rivers. Germs. Sassafras trees. Bones, blood and billiard balls. Dust and dogs. Icicles. Pagans. Shoelaces. Men traveling "in time" through "outer space" to other planets.

Certainly such things behaved as "matter." Certainly they looked, sounded and felt like "matter."

They were grainy or hard. Green or far away. Wet or furry. Recent or cold.

"But what *is* matter?

"What is the 'it,'" Mr. Quattlebaum demanded of himself, "which we call smooth or soft, red or nearby, dry or bald, ancient or warm?

"Is it atoms and molecules?

"But of what?

"Protons? Neutrons? Ions? Stuff? Energy?

"But what are they? Basically, I mean."

He turned onto the gravel road which led to his farm. Just short of the gate, lining the west side of the road, were his little sassafras trees. He stopped the car, got out, crossed the road and began with uncustomary care to examine a particular, actual, physical, material, real-for-sure sassafras tree.

"I am perceiving a sassafras tree," he said to himself, almost aloud, "out there in time and space.

"I *see* its dark-blue berries. Its yellow flowers. Its green, gold, crimson, elliptical, three-lobe and mitten-shape leaves. 'Out there.'

"I *hear* the snapping of its twigs. The rustling of its leaves. 'Out there.'

"I *smell* and *taste* its savory bark and roots. 'Out there.'

"I *feel* its soft, light wood. Its sticky foliage. Its oily bark. 'Out there.'

"I do indeed perceive this particular sassafras tree—looking, sounding, smelling, tasting and feeling 'out there' in a particular space at a particular time.

"But where are my perceptions? Are they 'out there'?

"No.

"My perceptions are 'in here'—in my own mind or consciousness.

"If they were 'out there'—out of my consciousness—they would not be perceptions at all. Perception means consciousness or awareness.

"Yet surely something causes these perceptions. Doesn't every effect have a cause? I don't really know. I must remember to look into that.

"But, even if every effect does have a cause, am I perceiving a cause of my perceptions—'out there'? No. I am just perceiving— 'in here.' I am just aware."

He did not believe that he was being unduly stubborn. He already had anticipated the probable reaction of his friends.

"Quattlebaum," they probably would say, "of course your perceptions are conscious. But won't you admit that they are caused by impulses reaching your brain from your sense organs through your afferent nerves and their complexes of axons, dendrites, synapses and ganglions?"

"Of course," he would reply. "But won't you in turn admit that what is true of the sassafras tree is equally true of afferent nerves and ganglions? Just as all perceptions of the sassafras tree occur only in consciousness, so it is only in consciousness that all causal impulses, organs and physiological paraphernalia—and all their causes—and, in turn, all *their* causes—can themselves be perceived, understood, known, deduced, hypothesized, confirmed, encountered or otherwise experienced."

His point was reminiscent of one made by an Irish bishop more than two centuries earlier: "Production of ideas or sensations in our minds can be no reason why we should suppose matter or corporeal substances, since that is acknowledged to remain inexplicable with or without this supposition."[1]

Mr. Quattlebaum could feel his hypothesis of the past few weeks jelling itself into a conviction.

"Men simply do not," he said to himself repetitiously, "and obviously cannot, experience anything outside experience. Men reason their way beyond many crude, original perceptions—but only by means of a refining process which itself is an exclusively conscious activity. Insofar as physical or material means non-mental, no man ever has experienced a single physical or material thing!"

But if a man could experience nothing outside experience—if he could perceive only his perceptions—then what, Mr. Quattlebaum began to wonder, was the real nature of the *content* of his perceptions.

He examined the sassafras tree again, this time more carefully and analytically, trying to determine which elements in his perceptions could be called most basic.

"First and perhaps most fundamentally, I perceive a tree. But how do I know it's a tree? Because it somewhat resembles all the other trees I have perceived. But how did I know they were trees? Because they, like this sassafras tree, possessed those characteristics which, as a group, connote a tree. But this tree is different from the others. Yes, but it is also similar—sufficiently similar so that this one and the others can all be called trees. Each, for example, has a trunk and bark and leaves. But doesn't this trunk differ from other trunks, this bark from other bark, these leaves from other leaves? Yes, but again there are similarities. They all seem to possess those characteristics which, as groups, connote trunk, bark and leaves.

"But this could go on all day—one group of characteristics or concepts after another. Perhaps it *does* go on all day. Perhaps one group of concepts after another is *all* that goes on. Let's have another look at the sassafras tree.

"I perceive the concepts of trunkness, barkness and leafness. If I were not perceiving these concepts, I would not and could not be using the words trunk, bark, leaves or tree to describe these masses of phenomena which I perceive. Perhaps, in fact, the concept of treeness is nothing but a combination of such concepts as trunkness, barkness and leafness. I also perceive the concepts of oiliness and stickiness. Otherwise, I would not and could not be calling this bark oily or this foliage sticky. If I were not also perceiving the concepts of greenness, goldness, crimsonness, ellipticalness, lobeness, threeness and three-lobedness, I would not and could not be describing these leaves. Nor could I identify these or any berries as berries if I were not perceiving the concept of berryness. Nor could I describe them if I were not perceiving such concepts as blueness, darkness and dark-blueness.

"Actually," speculated Mr. Quattlebaum, "concepts seem to be any and all of the characteristics which can be found in different contexts; and I suppose they could include, and perhaps do include, every characteristic of everything in the universe.

"But have I yet found what is most fundamental in my perceptions of the sassafras tree? What is the 'basic thing' *of which* these thousands of concepts are characteristics?"

Again he examined the sassafras tree, and tried to push an analysis of his perceptions still farther.

"Well, I'll be damned," he concluded. "I perceive *no* 'basic thing' of which my perceptual concepts are mere characteristics. I perceive only the characteristics—only the concepts themselves—in the many sub-combinations and in the total grouping which constitute this whole sassafras tree."

He also perceived that he would be late for dinner. He turned his car toward home. It had been an odd afternoon. He had not even reached the gate. It would be difficult to explain to Gertrude why he had spent the whole time standing by the road looking at sassafras trees instead of gathering firewood and rhubarb as he had promised.

As he neared the city he was wondering whether, fundamentally, groups of concepts might be all that men really mean by "objects." It now seemed clear to him that the words "sassafras tree" referred not to an object or to stuff or to a "thing" which merely "possessed" a certain combination of concepts, but rather to the concepts themselves—which, perceived in consciousness in varying combinations, were called "objects" (sassafras trees, for example).

"The thing, as apart from all appearances, seems to be a mere nothing . . . Why regard the thing as a something 'in itself' at all? Why not (be content to) find the thing *in* phenomena . . . ?"[2]

Was it not possible, he wondered—was it not in fact probable— that men's words had evolved as symbols not so much for "things" or various instances of "stuff" as for concepts and groups of concepts? For it seemed to him that, without such "shorthand" symbols for mental concepts and groups of mental concepts, men would be overwhelmed by unmanageable mental detail—and virtually unable to converse or communicate.

Converse or communicate?
With whom?
Mr. Quattlebaum had a new problem.

19. *Mr. Quattlebaum Tries To Go Out of His Mind*

Was he horribly alone?

If he could experience nothing outside his own field of consciousness, perhaps everything in the world of which he was conscious existed only in his own little mind—his friends, his home and car, his favorite fishing flies, perhaps even his wife and children.

He did not swell with pride at the prospect of occupying the one and only seat in the theatre of the world.

But he did not easily despair.

After all, there did seem to be other persons and other things. Other persons (or what seemed to be "other" persons) also seemed to have fields of consciousness like his. They seemed to experience and to reason and to respond to similar things in similar ways.

But where was this "seeming"?

He had to admit that all of his encounters with "other" persons and with "other" things were experienced only in his own field of consciousness. If he could experience nothing beyond his own experience, how could he hope to find evidence that events, things or "other" persons did or could exist outside his own mind?

For the first time in his life he wanted to go literally out of his mind—and he wasn't sure it was possible.

Then came a promising thought: why and how did it happen that "other" persons so often reached identical logical conclusions from identical premises?

After dinner Mr. Quattlebaum picked up the telephone and called nine friends. To each he said:

"Hi. This is Quat. Will you do me a favor? Will you help me go out of my mind? I'll explain later. Assume for the moment that all men are mortal and that Socrates was a man. What can you infer from those premises? Thank you very much. I'll explain next week. I'm in a hurry. Thanks again."

All nine friends reached the single conclusion that Socrates was mortal.

"Obviously," Mr. Quattlebaum concluded, "the laws of logic are operative somewhere beyond my own field of consciousness. I admit that it was only in my own field of consciousness that I perceived that an identical, valid inference from identical premises was drawn individually by my nine friends. But it was not in my field of consciousness that any of those nine acts of thinking occurred."

He was conscious of the *result* of the thinking of his nine friends, but he had not been conscious of the thinking itself. Yet it had occurred. Nine friends had reached the same conclusion from the same set of premises—a conclusion beyond caprice, with a unanimity beyond mere chance, inferred in a field or fields of consciousness beyond his own.

Mr. Quattlebaum was convinced that the world was not in him alone, and that he was not alone in the world.

He was convinced that he had company.

20. Who "Thought Up" the Laws of Thought?

"I—*and* my fellow men," Mr. Quattlebaum smiled—"experience and think about things: things encountered only in consciousness, things comprised of mental concepts, things like my sassafras trees, things which we call things only because they are groups of concepts."

But how, he wondered, were concepts grouped?

Did someone just decide to group trunkness and branchness with twigness and leafness? Or did such concepts group themselves? And, in either event, according to what principle or law if any?

Was principle or law found only in men?

Or did principle or law exist in the world which men perceived?

The common assumption that man "abstracts" concepts—that he "puts them into" or "pulls them out of" his perceptions—merely raised twelve further questions for Mr. Quattlebaum:

Why should man want to abstract concepts into or out of his perceptions at all? And how could man possibly know how to go about the abstracting of concepts? According to what principle, if any, did man abstract them? Was such a principle man-made? If so, was it made arbitrarily? If not arbitrarily, then in accordance with what prior principle? And what was *its* sanction? If such a principle was not man-made, what were its source and sanction? If man abstracted such concepts in accord with any principle, from or into what prior order or disorder did he abstract them? (After all, merely to have existed was to have existed in *some* order or disorder.) If there had been a prior order, had it been determined by any principle? If so, what had been that principle? And what had been its source and sanction?

As he neared the end of an hour's walk in a gentle rain, answers to all twelve questions seemed implied in a single observation:

"Man can and does gather concepts into groups," Mr. Quattlebaum observed. "Into clocks, for example. Into bowling balls. Into arguments. Into electric razors and interplanetary journeys.

"But he seems able to do so only in obedience to 'grouping laws' to which the concepts themselves seem subject—and which in fact seem to be a part of the very nature of concepts.

"For example, man cannot build or assert an object to be simultaneously a cube and a sphere. The necessary relationships which are perceived to exist between such concepts as cubeness and sphereness—and which seem to be a part of their very nature—include, in this instance, a necessary mutual exclusiveness."

Mr. Quattlebaum was aware that such logically necessary relationships between concepts often were called the laws of thought. But he was beginning to believe that this was a misleading phrase —because "what is important is not the fact that *we think* in accordance with these laws, but the fact that (concepts) *behave* in accordance with them."[1]

"It was not I," Mr. Quattlebaum shrugged, "who built the sassafras tree by grouping ten billion concepts (trunkness, branchness, greenness, etc.) into a rational arrangement. I merely perceive the sassafras tree, some of whose component concepts seem related to others by logical necessity—the same kind of logical necessity which dictated to my nine friends the conclusion that Socrates was mortal, once they had assumed that all men were mortal and that Socrates was a man.

"My nine friends did not inject reason into their premises. They found it there. They did not actively add the conclusion that Socrates was mortal. They merely perceived that conclusion, which was dictated by the logically necessary relationships between the concepts of man-ness, mortalness and Socratesness.

"Had this not been so, my nine friends would not have reached

—because they could not have reached (unanimously and independently)—their single, logically valid conclusion. They could have reached only a chaotic variety of meaningless non-sequiturs—or nothing."

So it was not man, Mr. Quattlebaum concluded, who nobly had drafted the laws of thought. It was not man who had imbued the world with reason. Man merely had perceived a world already imbued with reason—a world consisting of billions of concepts, a part of whose very nature had been a logically necessary interrelatedness—concepts which were what they were partly by virtue of their relationships with each other.

21. Where Was Whereness?

Where did concepts exist?

Mr. Quattlebaum had concluded that they were perceived by men only in fields of consciousness.

Yes, but now he was asking something else.

Where, he wondered, do concepts exist before men perceive them? Where are all the trillions of concepts, in all their quadrillions of logically necessary relationships, of which no man is yet fully aware? Where are all the things which men have yet to learn? Where, now, are all men's future concepts? Where were men's present concepts before they were perceived?

He strained in vain for answers—until he noticed something wrong with his questions. They were naïve.

For "whereness" and "when-ness" were concepts, too—like twigness and barkness and man-ness. In effect he had been asking "where and when is whereness?" and "when and where is when-ness?"

"Actually," Mr. Quattlebaum suddenly perceived, "there cannot be a 'where' where the sum-total of concepts exists.

"Nor a 'when' when they all exist.

"Because whereness and when-ness are themselves concepts. They are concepts of relationship between *other* concepts. They are a part of the sum-total of concepts. They cannot be apart from or outside the sum-total of concepts—or it would not be the sum-total.

"So whereness and when-ness (space and time) exist within the totality of concepts (the total universe); *the total universe does not exist within space and time.* Otherwise (if we were to subtract space and time from the total universe), we no longer would be talking about the total universe at all.

"If all concepts (the total universe) existed in space and time, then the concepts of space and time themselves would be said to exist in space and time—and that particular space and that time in another space and time—and so on in a progression both infinite and meaningless.

"When I experience the concept of whereness, when-ness, here-ness, thereness, nowness, pastness or futureness, I simply experience a concept of relationship between still other concepts in my field of consciousness. When I perceive the whereness of the sassafras tree, I perceive a concept or concepts of relationship between two or more groups of other concepts: the group of concepts which I call the sassafras tree and the group of concepts which I call my chicken house (perceived to be 'just north' of the sassafras tree) or the group of concepts which I call my cabin (perceived to be 'some fifty yards northwest' of the chicken house)."

In any notion of a "physical" world existing outside consciousness, nothing seemed to Mr. Quattlebaum more basic than space and time. Yet now he found that he experienced even space and time only as concepts within his consciousness—mental concepts of relationship between still other concepts. "In consciousness and consciousness alone is there continuity; and only so far as Space-Time *is* consciousness has it duration."[1]

Never in all of men's history, he now believed, had any "physical" book or bridge or building or bomb been perceived or built or encountered or even hypothesized outside a field of consciousness. There simply had been no human experience of anything "out there" with which to compare the sense data of which men had been conscious only "in here." "We have no material in terms of which to conceive a physical world supposed to differ in kind from our sense-data, except the material furnished by the sense-data themselves. (And) the only space and time in which the physical causes of sense-data can be located is the space and time of the sense-data themselves."[2]

The reactions of a few friends to whom he had tried to explain his changing perspectives were about what Mr. Quattlebaum had expected.

Here on his desk, for example, was a reply to his latest letter to Dr. Reasner, who was enjoying an extended fishing trip in New England. He stared again at the last sentence:

"Why, then, Quat, do men's environments—including their own bodies—so persistently *seem* 'so physical'?"

22. Could Things Even
"Seem" Physical?

"Dear Doc,

"Glad to hear that your perceptions of New Englandness have included the concepts of good-weatherness and many-troutness. One should not intrude upon such a vacation. Believe me, I would defer this response until your return, were it not for your apparently sincere insistence upon a prompt reply.

"So here goes:

"If no shred of logic or experience can confirm that anything exists beyond consciousness, then why, you ask, do things so persistently *seem* physical. We have discussed this before. 'Seeming' is in consciousness. Nothing can seem to be or to resemble anything which is not within consciousness. Nothing experienced can be compared with or contrasted to anything not experienced.

"You ask why, if this is so obvious, men have not risen up to reject the notion of a physical world as groundless and gratuitous. If in all history no one has experienced a single physical thing 'out there in space and time,' you ask why the *concept* of materiality is so persistent.

"You answer your own questions.

"Man cannot be conscious of a material stuff beyond consciousness. What persists, in your own words, is the *concept* of materiality. And, as a concept, the concept of matter is as much a matter of consciousness as is the concept of spirituality or of consciousness itself.

"Your definition of matter as anything which occupies space and has weight does not damage this position. Space and weight are themselves concepts. The weight of a sassafras tree and the space which it occupies can be computed only in terms of relationships between the group of concepts which constitute the sassafras tree and other groups of concepts which constitute parts of its environment. And no one can experience weight or a heavy object or occupied space except within his consciousness.

"I will therefore assume, Doc—at least until your return—that you require no further comment on your observation that data are gathered through men's eyes, ears, noses, tongues and skins. Obviously they are. But it is not obvious, and it does not and cannot follow, that such data are gathered from a 'physical world'—or that the sense organs themselves are a part of a 'physical world'—of which no one has yet had even a fleeting, superficial experience.

"I enjoyed your allusions to Dr. Johnson and the skates. You ask why the shin-skinned doctor in effect snapped at Bishop Berkeley, 'The hell that was an idea of a rock, man; that was a rock!' And you ask why, when a man trips over his child's roller skates and falls downstairs, he yells 'Damn those skates!' instead of 'Damn those *concepts* of skates!'

"Well, Doc, did you tell yourself when you got out of bed this

morning that you were putting on a garment known as your under-
wear, a garment known as your shirt, a garment known as your
pants, and garments known as your socks and shoes? Did you say,
'I am now picking up pieces of sporting equipment known as my
tackle box and flyrod, and I am now engaged in that form of self-
propulsion known as walking—toward a member of that category
of phenomena known as streams'?

"Or did you just get up, get dressed and go fishing?

"In his daily routine a man is concerned with specifics—with
specific concepts and groups of concepts and with their specific
relationships both to each other and to the group of concepts which
he calls himself. His lack of time, reason, training or inclination to
think of such specifics in terms of concepts does not prove that
concepts do not in fact underlie and constitute his every experience. After all, a man who assumes that he believes in the existence
of matter 'out there in space and time' has little more time or
inclination to think of specific phenomena in terms of atoms and
molecules than to think of them in terms of concepts. And to say
that I share your belief in atoms and molecules as a relatively sound
hypothesis at this point in history is not to say that I believe they
are something 'out there in space and time' beyond consciousness
or that they are the most basic elements of reality.

"All of this borders upon what perhaps was intended to be your
most important question. You ask: 'the rocks, shins, skates, bumped
heads, bruised buttocks, sights and sounds, smells and tastes, arms
and legs, the whole "physical world"—is all this to be dismissed as
a mass of mere appearance, illusion or hallucination? Are men to
reject all their centuries of experience, all the hard-won hypotheses
of their natural sciences, as a mere pack of lies and misconcep-
tions?'

"Not at all, Doc.

"We need pay no such ghastly price, or any price at all, for an
honest acknowledgment that there is no reason to assume or imagine any physical or material thing existing 'out there in space and
time' independently of mind.

"The hypothesis that no such thing as matter exists outside consciousness does not adversely affect a single hypothesis of science and does not reduce by one iota the validity of any other intellectual, factual, moral, aesthetic or 'physical' finding, judgment or conclusion of man.

"I grant that most of man's conclusions about himself and his universe have been reached upon the supposition that corporeal substance or matter does indeed exist independently of consciousness. But no such conclusion becomes any less valid without that supposition. All such conclusions are conceptual—or they would not be conclusions. None is contingent upon an essential postulate of independently 'physical' reality. 'No plain man, (and) no man of science, hesitates to talk of things as existing and as having qualities as yet undiscovered.'[1]

"But such talk is daily 'shorthand.' To define matter as that which occupies space and has weight is not to disprove that, more fundamentally, matter may be groups of mental concepts having spacio-temporal and other intra-group and inter-group relationships which themselves are also mental concepts. 'There is no doubt about the laws of "matter;" there is no doubt about the fact that in dealing with physical things we are dealing with something real; but there is a great deal of doubt about whether the concept of matter is an intelligible explanation of the order of the universe.'[2]

"So again, Doc, with a tedious repetitiousness as deliberate as it may be presumptuous, I pose these questions:

"Upon careful, honest examination of human experience, must we not acknowledge that our bodies and environments do not even *seem* 'physically' independent of consciousness?

"If we experience all that we experience, is it not meaningless to say that anything which we experience 'seems' like anything which we do not experience?

"Is it not meaningless to speak of 'comparing' perceptions, which we experience, with only-guessed-at causes or counterparts, which we do not experience?

"When we talk about real, physical sassafras trees or human bodies, are we not talking in shorthand about certain groups of mental concepts which are, have been or could be perceived *as* such groups?

"Sassafras trees and human bodies are groups of mental concepts which we tend to think of *as* groups because we usually experience them not separately but in a contiguous conjunction. And 'when the bond between two (or more) ideas has become thus firmly riveted,' as John Stuart Mill phrased it, 'the facts or phenomena answering to those ideas come at last to *seem* inseparable in existence.'[3]

"And 'the conception I form of the world existing at any moment comprises, along with the sensations I am feeling, a countless variety of *possibilities* of sensation; namely, the whole of those which past observation tells me that I could, under any supposable circumstances, experience at this moment, together with an indefinite and illimitable multitude of others which though I do not know that I could, yet it is *possible* that I might, experience in circumstances not known to me.'[4]

"Is it not therefore a relatively permanent possibility of repeated perceptions which 'distinguishes our idea of substance or matter from our notion of sensation?'[5] For me a physical thing is a certain perceived, perceivable or conceivably re-perceivable grouping of mental concepts within our fields, or some field, of consciousness. Matter is a relatively permanent possibility of perception.

"Those are indeed very real roller skates which men endeavor to remove from very real stairs. And those are very real skunks which men endeavor to keep beyond range of very real noses. But, again, we cannot say that such physical objects are 'real' by virtue of any unconfirmable existence outside consciousness, but only because they are persistently contiguous groups of mental concepts which constitute a relatively permanent possibility of perception.

"You are sure to insist—and I will agree—that this still does not tell us *why* objects are a relatively permanent possibility of perception. You will demand to know what *makes* them so. But please first hear me out.

"Reasons for keeping skates off stairs and skunks from noses are commonly stated in very simple shorthand: men detest falling downstairs and smelling skunks. But more fundamental, beneath such shorthand, may be a compelling interplay of logic between the most relevant of the millions of concepts which constitute such objects in such relationships. Such an underlying and infinitely detailed logic, which may 'set up' the fall on the stairs as a virtually syllogistic conclusion from such premises as a-skate-on-the-stairs and a-man-in-a-hurry, may be the same logic which implicitly convinces rational men that they should avoid such relatively permanent possibilities of unpleasant perception.

"I anticipate your next question: how many men will be quickly content to think of matter as nothing but the continuing possibility of perception?

"Not many.

"Even of those who come to acknowledge that matter cannot be experienced 'out there in space and time' beyond consciousness, most will insist that it must be more than a mere possibility.

"Most such men will ask what kind of an *actuality* it is. And where the possibility resides before it becomes an actuality. And how and why the possibility endures. These are reasonable questions.

"I for one must ask '*where,*' if neither in my own field of consciousness nor 'out there in space and time' beyond consciousness, is the fire in my fireplace when I am not watching it?

"By 'where' I of course do not mean in what location in space beyond consciousness. You will recall my earlier acknowledgment —my insistence, in fact—that spatial relationship is itself a concept within consciousness. What I mean is that I must find an *explanation* of how a fire in my fireplace can exist only in consciousness and yet neither in *my* consciousness nor in that of any other human being. I confess some dismay at the prospect.

"But Clare Proffitt (who enviously asks me to convey his hope that you are snagging the biggest ones from every stream in New England) makes a promising proposal. He insists that we schedule a three-man in-depth confab on this whole business as soon as possible after your return.

"Meanwhile, Doc, in advance of such a discussion, I wish to

volunteer one acknowledgment—not merely in the interest of what I am sure is our mutual intellectual honesty, but also out of an admittedly selfish pride: you and Clare have every right (and I would want neither of you to doubt my recognition of that right) to insist that such a thing as 'physical matter' *may* indeed exist.

"I shall continue to insist that any supra-conscious existence of such 'physical matter' never will be, because it cannot be, confirmed in man's exclusively conscious experience. But I also shall continue to acknowledge that you and Clare are free to guess, argue or hypothesize that such 'physical matter' *might* exist, without confirmation in man's experience, simply because it is man's very nature—indeed man's inevitably, exclusively conscious predicament—not to be able to experience anything inexperienceable (which might nonetheless exist).

"Actually, however, my concession is anything but magnanimous. In behalf of the existence of *no* 'physical matter' (beyond consciousness) can you introduce a whit of evidence based upon even a tiny fragment of all scientific or other empirical or rational experience in the whole history of the universe.

"And certainly 'it is hard to see how observation can ever lead us to the unobservable, or how experience can ever prove the inexperienced and inexperienceable.'⁶

"To guess, argue or hypothesize that anything exists beyond the totality of necessarily interrelated mental concepts is to plead the cause of a possible undefined something which, in our very nature, we never can experience or know.

"A wholly arbitrary quest of seven thousand seven-legged, seven-eyed dragons in seven caverns of an imaginary mountain on a non-extant planet would be an enterprise no less promising. For 'it is only within the experienced world that the terms "existence" and "reality" have any applicability. Carried beyond that world they are empty sound.'⁷

"By the same token it is important that no claim of human infallibility be entered in behalf of any hypothesis. I'm sure you would agree, Doc, that a good hypothesis is one which seems to explain available facts and to enhance the search for further facts.

And that a better hypothesis is one which supplants a good hypothesis when it seems to explain more facts. And that even the best hypothesis remains tentative so long as men are less than omniscient.

"Meanwhile I would contend that a continued dualistic hypothesis—of mind *and* matter—can serve only to prolong and aggravate pretended irrationality in human life generally and in religion particularly. A monistic hypothesis affirming nothing beyond consciousness confines itself to men's experience. I have begun to suspect that it will 'explain more facts' (mind-body relationship, causation, determinism *vs.* 'free will,' purpose, good, evil, truth, god, etc.). And it seems to promise deeper and more precise understanding, new freedom from needlessly contradictory beliefs, and thus greater opportunities to get on with the business of progress, including religious progress. These are sweeping statements which we can examine in the weeks ahead.

"For the present I am content to insist that a hypothesis consonant with all of man's rational and empirical knowledge and experience certainly would seem to merit at least as much consideration as a hypothesis fraught with more insoluble conflicts and which, in its very nature, man never can confirm. 'A hypothesis which in the nature of the case is incapable of any conceivable test is the hypothesis of nothing.'[8]

"Yet 'where,' then, is the fire in my fireplace—while neither I nor any other man is watching it or feeling its warmth or hearing its crackles or smelling its smoke?

"If not 'out there in space and time' beyond consciousness—yet neither in my field of consciousness nor in that of any other human being—then *'where'?*

"It is important that we find an answer.

"We'll meet at Clare's—as soon as possible after you get back.

"Warmest regards as always.

"Quat"

23. Who Watched the Fire When
Mr. Quattlebaum Went Fishing?

Clare Proffitt died suddenly of a heart attack.

From the cemetery Mr. Quattlebaum drove to his little cabin on the lake—to be alone for the weekend.

He spread his sleeping bag over an army cot and wondered "where" old Clare was—now that he was dead.

"The group of concepts which constitutes his body is in the group of concepts which constitutes his casket, which I helped to carry to the group of concepts which constitutes his grave. But the group of concepts which did or do constitute his soul or mind or whatever —where is that? Gone to live with god? Enjoying the beatific vision? Clock-watching on a rock pile in a customs-station purgatory? Burning in hell?"

Such phrases nauseated him. But he still wondered. In the days ahead friends would be sure to say that much of Clare obviously "lived on" in the fields of consciousness of Mrs. Proffitt, Mr. Quattlebaum, Dr. Reasner and everyone else who had loved or hated him or just borrowed his lawn mower. But in what real sense? And did the *"whole* he" live on? Could there be such a thing as personal immortality? How? "Where?"

An owl and a mosquito screeched and hummed Mr. Quattlebaum to sleep.

At five a whole dead field of human consciousness was resurrected by the brassy miracle of an alarm clock. And he did what he always did on those too-few occasions when he could get away from his home or office to the farm. Practicing that peculiar combination of reason, faith and prayer which for centuries had kept men going onto lakes at dawn in the hope of extracting fish, he got up, built a big fire in his fireplace, walked down to the lake, flycast for about two hours, returned to the cabin, and found his tall, orange flames replaced by little blue pilot lights sprouting from pink coals, just right for his coffee pot and skillet of bacon.

"I'll be damned. This is what Clare and Doc and I were going to talk about at Clare's. 'Where' was my fire while I was fishing?"

He had come to realize that no man ever had perceived a fire, cabin, coffee pot or skillet of bacon except within such a man's field of consciousness. Yet neither he nor any other man had experienced this fire during his two hours on the lake. The door had been locked, and no one could have seen through the curtains. But there had been a fire. He had seen it start. He could feel the warmth which it must have thrown through the cabin in his absence. These glowing coals were its apparent residue. "Where" had it been?

To friends he often had contended that to ask the location of the sum-total of mental concepts was to ask a false question. Location was spatial. And spatial relationship, or "whereness," was itself a concept. "Whereness" was therefore within consciousness. It could not be in a "place" beyond consciousness—where, so to speak, there could be no whereness.

Yet Mr. Quattlebaum believed that he was now asking a question which was not false or meaningless. He was not asking where whereness was. He was asking where his fire had been when he went fishing. It seemed a proper question.

The fire was a "physical object," which to him meant a group of logically related mental concepts perceived, or constituting a continuing possibility of being perceived, in consciousness. When *he* perceived his fire, in *his* field of consciousness, it was easy for him to determine the "location" of that group of mental concepts. It enjoyed many spatial relationships with still other groups of concepts: with the andirons, log pile, chimney and so on.

But "where" was his fire when *no* man perceived it?

It could never be proved to exist beyond consciousness, because beyond consciousness there was neither a "where" nor anything else experienceable by man.

But if the fire had existed within consciousness—yet neither within his own field of consciousness nor within that of any other man—then in *whose* or in *which* consciousness? Who or what had "watched" the fire, so to speak, when Mr. Quattlebaum went fishing?

An hour or so after he normally would have had breakfast, he was still reflecting upon his new insight or hypothesis or queer little notion or whatever it was.

"If the whole damned universe were one, big . . .

"Could it be that . . . ?

"A conscious universe?

"Everything in one vast mind?

"One all-inclusive, all-embracing field of consciousness?

"A conscious universe excluding nothing—not even nothingness?

"A conscious universe including everything and everyone? Including *all* concepts—man-ness, armness and legness? Treeness, atomness and flameness? Planetness and spaceness? Including all *groups* of concepts—all men, arms and legs? All trees, atoms and flames? All planets and space?

"Including the fire in my fireplace—while I was fishing?"

At first blush he seemed to have stumbled onto a possibly valid solution of his problem.

But Mr. Quattlebaum was an intellectually honest man. He tried to avoid wishful thinking. He wanted to be sure that he was not just "using words" to explain the location or status of phenomena which he believed could exist only within a field of consciousness, but which obviously did not always exist in his or in another man's field of consciousness.

While he loved good poetry, which he believed could reflect or "touch upon" large truths, it was not in his nature to be content with mere hints or suggestions of truth, however provocatively or aesthetically expressed. He had great respect for a Millay who could write that "if ever I said, in grief or pride, I tired of honest things, I lied."[1] But he had even greater respect for any honest effort to define the "honest things" themselves. He was as eager as a

Millay "to drink into (his) eyes the shine of every slanting silver line"[2]—to "split the sky in two and let the face of God shine through."[3] But he was not impetuously convinced by a Millay that Euclid alone had "looked on Beauty bare." For when "but far away (he) heard her massive sandal set on stone,"[4] he had to wonder *what* he heard. And this was what he had to seek.

He suffered no illusions of potential omniscience. He even wondered at times whether it was a waste of energy to look for ultimates which perhaps no man could ever reach. But he disliked being told, by men no closer to omniscience than he, that it was the very nature of such ultimates to be humanly incomprehensible—and that even honest conjecture about them must therefore be presumptuous or pointlessly naïve.

For how could they know? If they were right—if ultimates were beyond even the intelligent *conjecture* of man, if they were "mysteries" *inherently*—then how could any man have learned enough about them to tell another how much about them could not be learned?

What could they have in mind, he wondered—those priests and theologians, those ministers and rabbis, those conformingly fundamentalist laymen—when they asked their fellow men, "Do you believe in god?" If they meant a god not only undefined, unfathomed and unconjectured—but also indefinable, unfathomable and unconjecturable—then why did they seem so saddened by so frequent an answer of "I don't know"?

Surely, he thought, they could not wish to encourage their fellow men to pretend to believe what they neither conceived nor could conceive. Surely they could not wish to discourage their fellow men from honest meditation upon the possible nature of their world. For surely, in trying to do either of these things, they would be wasting their time—and wasting the whole world's time. For men would continue to wonder—and to try to understand. And Mr. Quattlebaum was one of them.

He began again to examine his notion of a conscious universe.

Could it be, he wondered, that everything in the universe existed in one vast mind?

That everything—in one vast mind—*was* the universe?
Everything?
All the mental concepts of which all "objects" seemed to be constituted?
In all the logically necessary relationships by which such concepts were meaningfully bound together, and of which some seemed actually to be constituted: spacio-temporal relationships, self-identities, similarities, differences, chemical attractions and repulsions, speeds, reasons, implications, conclusions?
Total mind, total reality—a fusion in total order?
Every part of which, every mental concept in which, was related to every other in—and by—logical necessity?
The totality of reason, logic, fact—in one all-inclusive, ultimate, necessary coherence?
The one master context *for* everything and *of* everything—and which *was* everything—and which was *why* everything was what it was?
It seemed to him that toward some such hypothesis—in a veritable lava of logic—flowed the *continuum* of all previously perceived emissions from the still-young volcano of man's total experience—the continuum of man's consciousness of concepts and of groups of concepts internally related by logical necessity, in ways and degrees increasingly apparent with the passing of each century and hour.
Not a total mind separate from or merely analogous to a human mind.
Just mind.
A single entity.
A single, conscious continuum of mental concepts—interrelated, in countless sub-contexts within the master context, by logical necessities both determining and determined by the logical necessity of the whole.
Total experience, total knowledge—everything experienced and known by men, and everything not yet experienced or known by men.
Total experience which was timeless and self-caused because, being complete, it contained all time and cause, none of which

could be said to exist outside total experience unless total experience were not total.

A universe in which to know or to be known was to be—and in which to be was to know or to be known.

A universe all of whose parts were so universally related as to leave no loose ends.

A universe which would not be the universe if deprived of any of its parts.

A universe none of whose parts would be real in isolation from the total.

A universe no part of which could be rationally understood unless all parts were rationally understandable—because no part could be what it was apart from its logical relationships with all other parts and with the whole.

Could this be the way it was—the way things were? Not figuratively or poetically or pseudo-poetically—but really?

Mr. Quattlebaum could envision a whole host of plausible objections, particularly from the camps of traditional religions. But he had a hypothesis on his hands. And the only honest thing to do with it was to put it to some tests.

How for example could he himself—or any other human person or self—fit into such a vast whole of ordered consciousness?

"What *is* a 'self'?" he asked himself.

24. *What Was a Quattlebaum?*

It was an odd way to spend an evening—sitting there asking themselves who or what they were.

But Mr. and Mrs. Quattlebaum found some interesting answers.

"What do we really mean," they asked, "when we say that we

are persons or selves or individuals or personalities? What do we mean by 'we' or 'I' or 'you'? What and where is each individual 'soul' or 'mind'?"

Neither was able to find a stripped-down mind which he could identify as a container of his thoughts or experiences. Neither could find a spiritual essence floating about within himself which he could identify as a soul. Neither could find a pure ego which "had" experiences, any more than Mr. Quattlebaum had been able earlier to find any pure matter which "had" characteristics.

Just as Mr. Quattlebaum earlier had failed to find in his sassafras tree any matter which "possessed" certain characteristics (but rather had found it comprised apparently of *no more than* certain characteristics or concepts—such as trunkness, barkness, leafness, brownness, greenness, etc.), so now he found that he could experience no mind or soul or pure ego which he could call a possessor or container of his thoughts or experiences. He could find nothing *but* his thoughts and experiences. "The Ego that pretends to be anything either before or beyond its concrete psychical filling is a gross fiction and mere monster and for no purpose admissible."[1]

If the universe were the rationally ordered total field of consciousness, then it seemed to Mr. Quattlebaum that a person or self was simply an incomplete but relatively integrated group of concepts constituting an individual field of relatively ordered consciousness which was within, and a part of, the total conscious universe.

Mr. Quattlebaum began to think of a person or self as a group of concepts only relatively integrated and ordered because the number of such concepts and the quality of their ordering obviously must fall far short of the number of concepts in the total conscious universe, and far short of the quality of their ordering—and also because of the varying degrees of experience, education and "physical" and mental health among human persons.

While he recognized such variations in degree, he certainly regarded both personal wisdom and personal health as shorthand terms with which to allude to the extent to which personal groups of concepts were well or poorly integrated—whether groups of concepts "in the mind" or those groups of equally mental concepts which comprised parts of the "physical" body.

It seemed to him that some selves were more selves than others —by virtue of their grasping or embracing more, or being constituted of more, of the total conscious universe. A self, he thought —like happiness—was developed not by self-consciousness, but by a growing human consciousness of more and more of the content of the conscious whole. A self was a half-way house (or a trillionth-of-the-way house) on the way to complete knowledge of total truth. And "there seems to be no feature in our experience whatever which is entirely excluded from entering into the constitution of what is felt as the self."[2] Even its environment was not something "around" the self; it was a part of the "self itself."

Each person, Mr. Quattlebaum speculated, was both an object and a subject—infinitely dependent yet infinitely important. He was an object because he was a part of the experience of others. He was a subject because he had experience of which those others were a part. He was infinitely dependent because he was nothing except by virtue of being a part of the total conscious universe, of which all other persons were comparable parts. Yet he was infinitely important because, without him, the total conscious universe would not and could not be the total universe—and, unless he were precisely what he was, neither the total universe nor any person or thing could be precisely what it was.

As an incomplete field of consciousness, the human person— body and soul—seemed to Mr. Quattlebaum to be a sub-context of mental concepts within the master-context of the total conscious universe. In a sense "the mind is a little thing, a mere item in an infinite universe . . . (but also) an infinite thing, the whole universe (potentially) within it."[3] And part of what was "in" the human mind seemed to Mr. Quattlebaum to be those necessarily related concepts which, in persistently contiguous aggregates, were called "physical" human bodies.

If, as Mr. Quattlebaum believed, consciousness was the only repository of "being" (of "physical" being as well as of "spiritual" being), then it was only in total consciousness—only in universal

mind—that truth and cause and fact existed. And it was only universal mind with which man's own consciousness or being could be
consonant—of which, so to speak, it was a segment.

Whatever man might learn (that food nourishes, that fire burns,
etc.) he thus would seem to learn only by becoming conscious of
facts or truths or "laws of nature" which existed in universal consciousness.

To Mr. Quattlebaum it seemed that men were able to communicate with each other, and with their rational-spiritual-"material"
environment, only because the total (men *and* environment) was
cut of a single cloth—the cloth of consciousness-in-common. Because men experienced no such thing as non-conscious "matter,"
they could experience no such thing as "interaction" between such
matter and consciousness. On the other hand, the possibility of
interaction of consciousness with consciousness (or the interaction
of concepts within consciousness) seemed to him not only virtually
limitless but logically mandatory.

So he began to believe that a specific man must "be" a field within
total consciousness, rather than "possess" a field of consciousness.
To speak of a "possession" of consciousness suggested a possessor
who existed outside consciousness—and this, he had insisted, there
was no right to assume and no reason to suppose. Neither his
experience nor his reason informed him of any person residing
outside consciousness, who could somehow find his way "in"—to
acquire an isolated field of consciousness of his own. But, by virtue
of "being" fields of consciousness, men could be in touch with truth,
could be a part of truth, and could be in touch with each other. They
could be their experience. Their experience could be they.

To the extent that two men communicated, Mr. Quattlebaum
believed, they actually identified. To that extent some of the concepts of which they consisted were identical concepts in each. The
two men "overlapped." To that extent the two men were one man.
Yet they were two men in those vastly more numerous instances
of their comprising differing concepts and concepts in differing
relationships.

Each man, it seemed to Mr. Quattlebaum, was a unique individ-

ual by virtue of the unique combination of concepts which constituted his experience—which indeed was *he*. Yet no man was the
unique "owner" of any of those concepts. They were "needed," so
to speak, in the millions of other contexts in total mind. They were
communal. Without them there could be no communication, no
truth and no men.

To have thought of a human mind or soul as a part of the private
property or equipment of a physical man—as being somehow
housed or "wrapped" in a physical body, or "plugged into" it by an
inexplicable but somehow "divine" kind of electronics—this would
have been to fall back upon the unwarranted presumption that a
man's body was a non-mental "physical kind of something," which
in fact no man ever had experienced. Mind, and what was "in"
mind, were not experienced as two separate entities. Mind was not
like a bucket "containing" fish. Ideas were not like garments "contained" in a closet. Consciousness was a fusion of container and
contained. "There is no distinction between subject and object,
between the knowing and what is known."[4] Merely to be conscious
was to be conscious of something. And all of men's experience
suggested that merely to be something was to be known.

Nor could Mr. Quattlebaum find anything in human experience
which suggested that mind and reason were two separate entities.
Reason did not seem to be a refining activity which a mind employed like a tool in order to "work on" mere "lifeless lumber"
perceived by mind. Such a tool would be like a hammer vainly
struggling to strike itself. And, since mind was not a perceiver
separate from the perceived, how could it perceive "lifeless lumber"
anyway? "Life"—in the form of logically necessary relationships
between the "lumber's" components, and between the "lumber"
and the other groups of concepts to which it was related—seemed
already present in the "things" perceived.

The existence of logically necessary relationships between certain concepts seemed to be not only concomitant, but perhaps
identical, with the act of their conscious perception. He suspected
that existence, perceptibility and perception might be a single phenomenon in consciousness, a single conscious phenomenon, a sin-

gle consciousness phenomenon. He acknowledged, of course, that much which might be perceptible in total mind had not yet become actual perception in every or any human mind. But wasn't this the difference, he wondered—perhaps even the only difference—between total mind and specific human minds or souls or selves? And when anything in total mind came also to be perceived in a human mind, did anything really occur except identification? Human learning seemed to be identification of parts of partial fields of consciousness with parts of the total field of consciousness.

Thus it seemed to Mr. Quattlebaum to be a part of the very essence of each self constantly to tend toward completion of the process of literal identification with the total conscious universe, of which each self was an ever-expanding segment or sub-context.

But in so speculating he did not commit the "teleological fallacy." He neither denied nor presumed purposiveness where purposiveness might or might not exist. He neither denied nor presumed that the self's apparently continuing tendency to identify with the total universal mind was due to any abstractly noble or externally superimposed motive. If a self were a field of consciousness comprising logically related concepts, and if it were a part of the total field of consciousness comprising *all* logically related concepts, then it seemed to him plausible that the self might be drawn by logical necessity toward identification with the complete rational context (of which it was literally a part)—just as a logically implied conclusion was drawn irresistibly from the premises of a syllogism.

However far off might be the point at which human selves might identify with the entire conscious universe, it seemed to him that such "parts" had been manifesting the timelessness of the "whole" for many centuries. Surely, he thought, the self has "a temporal continuity which goes far beyond anything that can be immediately experienced at any given moment . . . it stretches out both into the past and the future beyond the narrow limits of the 'sensible present.' "[5]

And as it stretched into past and future—farther and farther into the total, timeless, conscious universe of which it thus became a larger and larger part—the self apparently ceased to remain the smaller entity which it had been. "The permanent identity of the self is a matter of degree . . . it is possible for me, even in the period between birth and death, to lose my old self and acquire a new one, and even to have more selves than one, and those of different degrees of individual structure, at the same time."[6]

Mr. Quattlebaum found himself wishing more than ever that those who spoke glibly of immortal souls would be more careful to define what they really meant by immortality *and* souls. He could see that a growing self or soul—which was a part of a total, timeless consciousness—would be in a sense immortal *ipso facto*. But a soul envisioned as a little blob of pure spirit—or as some sort of spiritual "organ" which somehow was strengthened by virtue or which picked up sin like lint—seemed hardly worthy of the word.

On the other hand, he wondered, how worthy was his own notion of a soul or self?

In which bizarre directions might his logic be leading him?

He had concluded tentatively that a self was a relatively small but logically integrated group of those very concepts which, in their totality, comprised the entire, vast, conscious universe. And tentatively he believed that each such concept existed not only in, but by virtue of, an all-embracing, uncuttable net of mandatory, inescapable, logically necessary relationships with every other such concept.

Where, then—within a total context so exhaustively characterized by logical necessity—could there be room for "freedom" of a self?

How, Mr. Quattlebaum asked his good wife, could such apparently enslaved "selves" be "free" to "cause" whatever they might "will" to "cause"?

"I only know," she replied, "that you always have thought yourself quite 'free' to 'cause' the balls on Dr. Reasner's billiard table to perform in accordance with your 'will.' "

Mr. Quattlebaum thought it would be well to have a closer look at the meaning of "freedom" and of "will"—and at the nature of "cause."

IV

---

25. Dr. Reasner's Billiard Table

Mr. Quattlebaum chalked the cue, thrust it against the cue ball and glanced at the pocket into which he confidently expected the 7-ball to drop.

But at the instant of impact the 7-ball remained motionless, as if bolted to the table. And the cue ball stopped dead against the 7-ball, as if held to it magnetically.

The luxurious laugh to which Dr. Reasner had looked forward while setting the stage for his practical joke was aborted by the quietness of Mr. Quattlebaum's perceptive reaction.

"You've gone to some bother, Doc. You drilled a hole in your nice pool table, ran this big bolt up through the hole and into this trick 7-ball, and paid dearly to have a magnet recessed into a trick cue ball. I sense you may be trying to tell me something."

Dr. Reasner. I thought you'd enjoy being the first man in history to participate in this dramatic discrediting of a "law of nature."

Mr. Quattlebaum. How have I discredited a "law of nature"?

Reas. You said on the phone you were reading about causation. I assumed you would get around to Hume.

Quat. I have.

Reas. Then you know he was a pool player.

Quat. I do.

Reas. Do you remember this passage? "The first time a man saw the communication of motion by impulse, as by the shock of two billiard balls, he could not pronounce that the one event was *connected:* but only that it was *conjoined* with the other. After he has observed several instances of this nature, he then pronounces them to be *connected.* What alteration has happened to give rise to this new idea of *connexion?* Nothing but that he now *feels* these events to be *connected* . . . and can readily foretell the existence of one from the appearance of the other."[1] You also may remember this: "The first instance which we saw of motion communicated by the shock of two billiard balls . . . is exactly similar to any instance that may, at present, occur to us; except only, that we could not, at first, *infer* one event from the other; which we are enabled to do at present, after so long a course of uniform experience."[2]

Quat. Go on.

Reas. Wasn't Hume saying, and isn't natural science saying, that we never really understand *why* a cause causes an effect? "Experience only teaches us, how one event constantly follows another; without instructing us in the secret connexion, which binds them together, and renders them inseparable."[3] We find no "necessary bond." We just say it's a "law of nature" that, in similar circumstances, similar consequents or "effects" follow similar antecedents or "causes."

Quat. Is this the "law of nature" which I am presumed to have discredited?

Reas. Well, do you know of any other pair of billiard balls which remained motionless after such impact? Hume says we can "infer . . . after so long a course of uniform experience"[4] an effect quite different from the one you "caused." Haven't you discredited a long-recognized "law of nature"?

Quat. Where is the law which decrees that a billiard ball must move when struck? The word "law" is only a shorthand symbol of the fact that, in similar circumstances, one kind of event repeatedly follows another kind of event. But in this instance the circumstances were not similar. You altered them by bolting down the 7-ball and magnetizing the cue ball.

Reas. Surely you don't mean that *I* have amended a "law of nature"—or discovered a new one?

Quat. No. I mean that determination of cause and effect requires no use of the word "law" at all. You can't phrase a "law" to describe all similar instances of cause and effect unless you first know what it is about such instances which makes them similar. But if you first know what makes them similar, then why phrase a "law"? It can only summarize what you already know.

Reas. Then you don't agree with Hume or with natural science? Aren't they saying that we must *repeatedly* observe instances of a similar sequence of events before we can assume a cause-and-effect relationship?

Quat. I agree with science but not with Hume. It is proper for the natural scientist repeatedly to observe things and events, to record apparent similarities in their sequences, to pose tentative cause-and-effect hypotheses, and to formulate experiments to further test such hypotheses. But, while it is thus proper for the scientist to seek *instances* of cause and effect, it is not his job to philosophize upon the *nature* of causation. That is the province of philosophy.

Reas. Hume was a philosopher.

Quat. But mistaken, I believe, on several counts. We can observe an event which we do *not* call an effect of an immediately preceding event. I cast my bait into the reeds. Then I open a can of beer. Then a bass grabs the bait. Do I catch the bass "because" I opened the can of beer immediately beforehand? Or because of the bait which previously had been placed in the vicinity of the bass? And you may recall Bertrand Russell's chicken. For weeks it was fed daily just after sunrise. It may have concluded that being fed was a regular "effect" of dawn—until, just after an otherwise typical sunrise, its neck was wrung. Was either its breakfast or its death an "effect" of dawn? We also can observe repeated instances of an event which consistently appears to "cause" a certain "effect" but which sud-

denly leads to a result quite different. Although Hume says "we are
enabled to infer . . . after so long a course of uniform experience"[5]
that one billiard ball struck by another will roll, one failed to do so
a few minutes ago, as we observed. I conclude that it is not a merely
superficial or large-scale similarity of events, but rather the specific
respects in which they are similar, which are responsible for their
"causing" understandable "effects." A single performance of your
bolted and magnetized billiard balls is enough to reveal a unique
cause-and-effect relationship different from one which would exist
if the bolt and magnet were not present. I dispute Hume's insistence
that repeat performances are required.

Reas. I agree that we suspect some cause-and-effect relationships
rather promptly, without repeated demonstration. We often *feel*—
we often have a sense of *knowing*—that one event really "causes"
another, whether it immediately precedes it or not. I agree that by
cause we mean "not just a series of links (but) the *linkage* that joins
the links . . . some pushiness, something dynamic, efficacious, which
brings about the effect."[6] I agree that "there is a sense attaching
to the term causality in its everyday usage which cannot be satisfied
to drop the reference to a connecting bond, or to effective agency."[7]
But I still don't know *why.* I'm as lost as William James. He felt
certain that cause meant more than "merely habitual time-
sequence,"[8] but he gave up and called it "an altar to an unknown
god; an empty pedestal still marking the place of a hoped-for
statue."[9] How's your sculpting, Quat? You say that it is not a
merely superficial or large-scale similarity of events, but rather
specific *respects* in which they are similar, that are responsible for
"causing" understandable "effects." But precisely what do you
mean by these "specific respects"?

Quat. As you know, Doc, I have found—in matter, things, mind
or persons—nothing but concepts. I have found no material "stuff"
which possesses properties, but only the properties themselves—or
concepts. I have found no mental "stuff" which contains thoughts,
but only the thoughts themselves—or concepts. I have found no
thing or self which appears to be more than a group of concepts.
Each concept appears to be related to others by logical necessity,

each necessarily deriving part of its very nature from the nature of its logically necessary relationships with others.

Reas. You would call two billiard balls, for example, two similar groups of similar concepts.

Quat. Yes, but not *entirely* similar. The 7-ball, for instance, differs from the cue ball in color and in identity. The 7-ball is one group of concepts: sphereness, weightness, reddish-brownness, whiteness and certain instances of relatedness to its fellow billiard balls and to its environment. The cue ball is another group of concepts: sphereness, weightness, whiteness and certain *other* instances of relatedness to *its* fellow billiard balls and to *its* environment. They resemble and differ from each other in certain "specific respects"—by which I mean the presence or absence of certain concepts, and the similar and different relationships between the concepts, which make up the groups and sub-groups of concepts which we know in shorthand as these particular billiard balls.

Reas. And, to use your terminology, tonight I added those concepts which constitute steel-boltedness to those concepts which previously constituted my 7-ball—and I added those concepts which constitute magnetism to those concepts which previously constituted my cue ball.

Quat. Yes. And our previous observations of the kind of behavior which attends a certain relationship between the group of concepts known as steel-boltedness and the group of concepts known as magnetism enabled you to predict, and me to explain, the 7-ball's motionlessness when struck by the cue ball and the cue ball's immediate adherence to the 7-ball. You knew your practical joke would work when you first thought of it, and I correctly suspected the concepts which were involved. We did not require repeat performances.

Reas. Didn't we? How could I have staged my show, and how could you have analyzed it, if we had not previously observed the principle of magnetism at work?

Quat. But we had not previously observed the entire large-scale phenomenon of a magnetized billiard ball striking a bolted-down billiard ball and of both then remaining motionless against each other. Despite Hume's contention to the contrary, we did not need such previous experience of the entire phenomenon. All that was needed, to stage or analyze your demonstration, was an awareness that *some* of the concepts in the group of concepts known as a steel bolt were *necessarily* so related to *some* of the concepts in the group of concepts known as a magnet that a certain "effect" would result from their being placed into the particular relationship which you chose.

Reas. Actually, then, you are saying that the cause-and-effect relationship is a logically necessary relationship between concepts —like that between the premises and conclusion of a syllogism.

Quat. Yes. If concepts are the only things in the world, they are the only things which can be related. The causal relationship is not a brute relationship between two or more large-scale things or events. It is a relationship of necessary logical implication among certain of the concepts of which large-scale things or events are constituted.

Reas. In a sense, then, a cause wouldn't seem to cause an effect any more than an effect would seem to effect a cause. There is just a relationship—*between* concepts. Is that what you're saying?

Quat. Exactly. And we merely use the word cause to designate the concept or group of concepts which, in a causal context, seems to precede the other in temporal sequence. The concept or group of concepts which seems to follow in such a sequence is merely called the effect. The essence of a cause-and-effect relationship is not temporal sequence, but the logically necessary relatedness of the concepts. In fact, in some such relationships it is difficult to say which is cause and which is effect. Does a steel-filled 7-ball cause a magnet-filled cue ball to cling to it? Or does a magnet-filled cue ball cause a steel-filled 7-ball to cling to it?

Reas. How do you suppose the whole thing got started, Quat? If the total universe consists of billions of concepts necessarily related by logical implication—full of billions of necessarily implied cause-and-effect relationships—didn't there have to be a *first* cause?

Quat. "First" in relationship with *what?* Are you wondering whether one of the causes within the total universe preceded all the others? Or are you wondering whether the total universe itself is the effect of a cause which exerted influence from outside the universe?

Reas. Either.

Quat. I would say neither. If all of the concepts which constitute the universe are necessarily related to others, none could be the very "first." To be a cause at all is to be causally related to something else, which therefore must exist simultaneously. On the other hand, to speak of the total universe as an effect of a cause existing outside the total universe is a contradiction. All causes—and time itself (and hence any "first moment" of time)—must exist *within* the total universe unless the total universe is not total. I must agree with Karl Pearson that to say "this is a first cause" is to say "here begins my ignorance."[10]

Reas. If the total universe is one vast field of total consciousness, made up entirely of concepts necessarily interrelated by logical implication—and if every man is a part of this all-inclusive web of inevitable logical necessity—then how can any man be free?

Quat. Gertrude has been asking me that.

26. *Fantaisie Capriccioso*

"And what do you say to Gertrude," asked Dr. Reasner, "when she asks how a man can be free in a freedomless world?"

"I have found it a good subject to exclude from domestic discussion," Mr. Quattlebaum replied. "I have asked what she really means by freedom and all that. But our progress has been slight."

Reas. My sympathies are with Gertrude. If, as you say, all things in the universe are interrelated by logical necessity, if all acts are mandated by compulsory "causes," if every act is the effect of a necessary cause, then it would seem to follow that every act of man's will is necessarily an effect of a cause—and thus not a completely "free" act of a completely "free" will. How do you escape this conclusion?

Quat. I don't.

Reas. Then you don't believe in a free will?

Quat. I haven't found one. Doc, if you and I and every other person had a "will" which was really "free"—*really* free, beyond the influence of causal factors, free right down to the bare bone of caprice—how could there be any truth or order in the world? How could there be a world at all? I have found, and I believe you will find, no such thing, no such independent entity, as an isolated will which is free to choose. Complete freedom is caprice. We are fortunate that a world full of capricious wills is a fantasy. Just as I view "matter" not as an autonomous "something" to which characteristics cling, but rather as grouped concepts—and just as I view the "self" not as a separate entity which "contains" consciousness, but rather as a field of consciousness—so I view the will not as an independent, undisciplined entity, but rather as an expression of logical conclusions implied in those "premises" which are the concepts which comprise the self. What else prevents men from "choosing" their way into instant chaos or destruction?

Reas. But whatever men choose they do *choose*. And choice means freedom. That's my point, Quat.

Quat. Choice means *restriction*. And that's *my* point, Doc. We choose. But we can't choose our choice. Someone—it may have been Hobbes—said we have the will to act but not the will to will. If a will is a power to choose, it is a power to choose rationally and from *something*. If it is a power to act, it is a power to act rationally and on the basis of *something*. A will is in a sense "free" when not arbitrarily enslaved by an external force or power; but it cannot be free from the rational, internal influence of which it is the very expression. The freedom which men most cherish is the freedom to express their own natures without undue external restraint. But a truly "free" will—wholly capricious, unresponsive and irresponsible because uncaused, undetermined and thus undisciplined—could thwart such expression of such natures as readily and arbitrarily as could any external compulsion or restraint. A man can be "free" to resist "immediate stimuli," but only because he is *not* "free" to resist the influence of his own "ideas of ends."[1] A man's will is not free from himself.

Reas. Which suggests that any freedom which the will may have is at least not the unqualified freedom which most of us have presumed.

Quat. And is qualified freedom really freedom?

Reas. But even if we agree that a man's will is not wholly free from the influences which stem from within his own nature, isn't it otherwise free to the extent that it remains unconditioned and undetermined by anything beyond itself?

Quat. I see no such distinction. As you know, Doc, I see each self—each human field of consciousness—as an incomplete group of the very concepts which constitute the total field of consciousness which I call the universe. All of these concepts, those within each self and those beyond, seem interrelated in bonds of logical necessity. If so, some (as "effects") are necessarily implied (as "causes") within each self. A man can perform only those acts which are "effects" of the man he has become. "All causes are, themselves, effects of earlier causes; if you choose as you do it is because you have become the sort of person you are. But now that you are that sort of person, it is you who are choosing. The links of causation go through your life."[2]

Reas. If all acts of man are effects of causes, why do we *feel* so free? Why is a man convinced that he votes for the candidate of his "choice," for example—or that he joins the church of his "choice"?

Quat. Because indeed he does. But he is unaware that his choices are caused. To be wholly free, a man would have to escape all influence, which of course is impossible. To *feel* free, he must *feel* uninfluenced. And he does feel uninfluenced, and thus free, when causal influences are not perceptible to him. There are millions of tiny, intricate causal factors which he does not perceive but by which he nevertheless is influenced: all of the environment, inherited traits, education, experience and training, for example, which constitute his "self." Note that he has a greater sense of freedom in voting for the candidate of his "choice" than in "choosing" whether to murder his neighbor. In weighing the latter "choice," he is much more aware of the grave consequences which perceptibly influence him as causal deterrents.

Reas. But if a man does not choose until his mind is made up, does he really choose at all? Doesn't the concept of human choice dissolve into unreality or absurdity?

Quat. On the contrary, isn't it an uncaused choice—a choice without cause, if such a thing were possible—which would be the essence of absurdity and of intellectual chaos? To make a caused choice is to act rationally. An irrational act of making an uncaused choice, a choice related to nothing, is an impossibility. The human mind can make what we call mistakes in logic, but it cannot work in a fundamentally irrational manner. And the will cannot make fundamentally irrational choices because the will is the mind—not darting fantastically from caprice to caprice, but "choosing" only what it "thinks." And this is why a man, so long as he is learning and maturing but not yet omniscient, "can never be absolutely certain beforehand *what* (he) shall choose."[3]

Reas. I'll ask this bluntly, Quat. Are you a fatalist?

Quat. No. Fatalists believe that nothing we do, caused or not, can affect an end which somehow is inexorably in store for us. I believe on the contrary that everything we do—or don't do—must have its effect upon our development.

Reas. Do you believe in predestination?

Quat. I don't even know what it means. To say that nothing we do, caused or not, can have any bearing upon the salvation of our souls—well, that calls for definitions of "soul" and "salvation." I cannot concede that any of man's endeavors is without effect.

Reas. But suppose that the whole world were suddenly to share your view that no man is free to make an uncaused choice or to perform an uncaused act. Wouldn't men give up the struggles of life in abject resignation, or give in to every irresponsible desire, because of a what-the-hell conviction that whatever will be will be? William James said that a view like yours "makes those who are already too inert more passive still; it renders wholly reckless those whose energy is already in excess."[4]

Quat. John Stuart Mill had an interesting answer for a similar question. If a man finds that he has no free will, won't he be discouraged and not try to succeed or reform? Mill noted that, if such a man desires to succeed or reform, he probably will; if he doesn't, he may not—but neither will he feel discouragement. But the real point, I think, is this: to discover that man is not free to make uncaused choices or to perform uncaused acts is not to discover any uselessness or irrelevance or ineffectiveness in the caused choices which he does make or in the caused acts which he does perform. On the contrary, every one of man's acts and choices *is* useful and relevant and effective precisely because it *is* causally related—in logically necessary relationships—with every other concept in the universe. Every choice and every act of every man is an effect caused by the rest of the universe; but by the same token the universe could not be the universe unless, in part, it were similarly the effect of every choice and of every act of every man. To discover in such a context that one is not free to make uncaused choices or to perform uncaused acts is not to be led into inert depression or into a life of crime. It is to be led toward greater mental health, toward more sensitive personal and social responsibility, and toward a deeper sense of religion.

Reas. Why don't you stop smoking?

Quat. I've tried.

Reas. How often?

Quat. Six or seven times. Are you suggesting that my disbelief in free will is because my own is weak?

Reas. Well, I . . .

Quat. How many times did you try to give up cigarettes before you finally succeeded?

Reas. Maybe five or six.

Quat. Why didn't you succeed the first time? Were you any less free to make your first choice than your fifth or sixth? If you and I freely chose an otherwise uncaused act of permanent abstention, why was *any* of our "free choices" aborted?

Reas. I suppose I tried harder the last time.

Quat. I don't believe it. And neither do you. You once told me that you nearly lost your mind in the course of your first two heroically self-sacrificing struggles to give up cigarettes, but that years later you quit smoking one morning with virtually unnoticeable forethought or effort. Your "stronger resolutions" failed. And your final success came almost passively.

Reas. But I had been thinking about it a long time—sometimes even subconsciously, I suppose.

Quat. Exactly. As a man named Sidgwick once pointed out, a sudden resolve to stop smoking is not what men vaguely call "will" at all. It is a sudden awareness of certain conclusions "caused" by certain premises in which they are logically implied.

Reas. Are you less aware than I of causal or logical relationships between cigarette smoking and lung cancer or heart attacks?

Quat. No. That's why each of us repeatedly has tried to break the filthy habit. But the two sets of causal factors which are involved —the hundreds of conceptual "premises" which constitute your "self," and the hundreds which constitute my "self"—are not identical and therefore do not lead to identical conclusions or "decisions." Each of us has been relatively comfortable without cigarettes while fishing, walking in the woods or listening to symphonies. But otherwise our situations have not been similar. Although you enjoyed a cigarette after surgery, for example, you had no opportunity to smoke while performing a two-hour lobotomy. But in the course of fighting deadlines ten hours a day at a desk, I have had the opportunity to smoke, have exercised it, and have become deeply addicted. And thus far my efforts to do a day's work without cigarettes have failed. Self-excuse? Perhaps. But my point is that no two "selves" comprise precisely the same two sets of logically, causally related concepts—and therefore do not reach precisely the same conclusions in the same way at the same time —and that judging one's neighbor in terms of strength or weakness of non-defined "will" is a risky business. As a matter of fact, as Sidgwick says, "the common belief (e.g. in the power of a resolution to break a habit) is really inconsistent with the very doctrine of free will that is thought to justify it: for if by a present volition I can fully determine a future act, when the time comes to do that act I shall find myself no longer free."[5]

Reas. If men are not really free—if all of their "choices" are really determined by logically necessary causes—isn't it ridiculous of society to pass laws which hold men responsible for their acts and which provide punishments for acts which they are not free to avoid?

Quat. On the contrary, Doc, wouldn't it be ridiculous to establish laws and punishments for men who really *were* free, who really *were* capable of holding themselves beyond the reach of all influences? It is *freedom* which "cannot be influenced by anything or it would not be 'freedom'—the idea of making laws for it, and of attaching to such laws penalties, is nothing less than absurd."[6] Laws and penalties make sense because we are *not* beyond influence. Our future acts are determined in part by motivational causes (anticipated satisfactions) and by deterrent causes (statutory and other threats of discomfort). A person who believes that we have truly "free" wills "has no right to assert that there is even a probability that the expectation of punishment will alter our volitions"[7]—simply because such a person, insisting that our power of choice between motives can be "free" and undetermined, is not entitled to say that any act is likely to result from one motive rather than from another.

Reas. I agree, of course, that he can't have it both ways.

Quat. He certainly cannot.

Reas. Actually, then, either to praise or to denounce a man for any act of completely "free" will would be meaningless and hollow. One would be bestowing unearned praise or denunciation upon an act of sheer caprice, which in fact was therefore neither meritorious nor evil. Is this what you're saying?

Quat. It seems so to me.

Reas. I believe I'll have to agree. If one's "will" could perform "free" from influence—all on its own, so to speak—then how, with a "bad" will, could one successfully will that his "bad" will become a "good" will? "If our will-impulses are as lawless, as capricious" as is contended by those of us who have professed belief in "free will," then "we may train ourselves never so patiently, and that little imp of a 'free will' may just as well jump the other way," whereas recognition of the universality of cause-and-effect "teaches us that every effort counts, that there is a mechanism of self-control."[8]

Quat. Yes, it is a *whole pattern* of factors by which volitions or "choices" or "decisions" are determined. It is not a single, merely instantaneous volition, but rather a man's *whole character*, which persists to be called right or wrong, in varying respects and in changing degrees. For the man who insists that there is a truly free will, "the volition . . . is a perfectly undetermined choice between two motives (but) when the volition is over, it has ceased to exist and it has not . . . left a permanent cause behind it."[9] So it is the believer in free will whose concept of morality is dangerously superficial. "The whole fabric of morality would be upset if our approval or condemnation of a man for his volition had no right to last longer than the volition itself."[10]

Reas. In other words, why should I be ashamed of or punished for something which I've done for *no* reason—something which is not literally a part of *me*? "Surely the more closely a defect is bound up with me, the more it is essential to my nature, the more reason I have to feel ashamed of it."[11]

Quat. And how fortunate it is that your will—your thinking—*can* be affected, as for example by remorse. Not a meaningless remorse—for a wild, unrelated, uncaused, arbitrarily "free" act of will—but a meaningful remorse for having been the kind of person you were, a remorse which is a by-product "effect" of your taking a closer look at the facts, and in turn a "cause" of rehabilitating advantages outweighing the momentary pain of a particular transgression.

Reas. Yes, and realization that there is no such thing as an undisciplinedly, illogically "free" will can helpfully and justly soften the emotion with which we presume to criticize our fellow men. It provides an insight into the sanction of "judge not lest you be judged."

Quat. And shows us the compatibility of condemning sin but pitying the sinner.

Reas. Which may be why "Jesus . . . combined an invariable intolerance of sin with an almost invariable compassion for the sinner."[12]

Quat. It's after two. I told Gertrude I'd be home by midnight.

Reas. You have a weak will.

Quat. It isn't free from the influences of interesting people.

Reas. And if it were free from influences, *really* free from causal factors, the whole concept of morality would be less meaningful rather than more so. Right?

Quat. It seems so.

Reas. To say that "the true moral status of a man" is something which remains related to a previous "bad mode of life" is to say that a man cannot be made better by good influences.[13]

Quat. And "a mode of thinking which compels us to deny the sanctity of St. Paul because it might never have existed but for the influence of Christ, of St. Augustine because it would not have existed but for St. Ambrose ... is more flatly opposed to the deepest moral convictions of mankind than the crudest and most mechanical theory of human conduct by which (a denial of free will) has ever been caricatured."[14] Can I have your silly pool ball as a memento?

Reas. Here. I've autographed it for you.

27. The Hat Rack

On his way home he paused under the street lamp at Sixth and Elm and smiled at the autographed billiard ball and its protruding bolt.

A police car stopped.

"Whereya goin', mister?"

"Home, thank you, officer. Just up the street."

"Whatcha got there?"

"This? Oh, this is a . . . sort of a modified billiard ball, I guess you'd say."

"Let's see. Nice handle, huh? Whatcha doin' out on the street with a thing like this at two-thirty in the morning?"

"A friend gave it to me, sir. He just rigged it up this way so he could . . ."

"Been drinkin'?"

"No, sir. I mean . . . you know . . . just a couple of beers at my friend's house."

"What's your name?"

"Quattlebaum."

"*Quattlebaum?* Get in. We'll run down to the station."

The police telephoned Gertrude, who panicked, and Dr. Reasner, who in a progressively frustrated attempt to explain the billiard ball finally yelled, "Oh, god damn it, he's a fine man—just let him go home!" He then talked himself out of a threatened charge of disrespectful interference with proper police procedures, and they all got to bed about four.

After a brief period during which Mr. Quattlebaum was not overly rational about the incident, he agreed that the logic of all participants had been impeccable. For Doc and himself it was true that a man was just innocently walking home from the house of a friend. For the policeman it was true that a man brandishing a dangerous weapon under a street lamp at 2:30 A.M. ought to be questioned. For Gertrude it was true that her husband had said he would be home by midnight and that a call from the police at 2:45 A.M. was valid cause for alarm.

Three differing notions of "the truth" had resulted from valid reasoning within three differing contexts. When the three contexts were broadened into a single, larger context, there was unanimous agreement as to the "truth" of what had happened.

The larger the context, the larger the truth? The smaller the context, the smaller the truth?

Mr. Quattlebaum began to think about that.

Was it possible that reason alone was not man's ultimate criterion of truth? It was the only test of truth which he had accepted early in his search, but he had accepted it hesitantly and tentatively.[1] He had felt that to dispute the credentials of reason as a valid test of truth would have been to dispute the credentials committee itself, and thus to have disputed all of man's past and present understanding and the possibility of future understanding of his universe— simply because comprehension by reason was the very meaning of understanding. Yet he had wondered whether reason as we know it might be "still evolving," still incomplete or immature, and hence an imperfect test of truth. He was now a little pleased that he had not begged the question.

The larger the context, the larger the truth? The smaller the context, the smaller the truth?

"But why should that be?" he asked himself. "Isn't truth truth? What difference does the size of the context make—so long as the hard, cold laws of logic are applied to all of the hard, cold facts?"

But was there such a thing as a "hard, cold" fact?

If, as Mr. Quattlebaum believed, the universe was the total field of consciousness, consisting of *all* concepts in all of their quadrillions of logically necessary interrelationships—and if, as he believed, each such concept derived a part of its own logically necessary nature from such relationships—then there could be no such thing as a complete concept except in the complete context of the total universe itself.

The concepts with which man was reasoning were real because they (and thus he himself) were a part of the totality of logically interrelated concepts which constituted the universe. But he was reasoning with *incomplete* concepts simply because he was not yet omniscient. There were implications in his reasoning, and within the concepts with which he reasoned, which were not yet a part of his fast-maturing but not-yet-mature knowledge.

It was, as Mr. Quattlebaum put it, as if all of the logically inter-related concepts which constituted the universe were a vast criss-cross of ropes. And as if all men, themselves consisting of fibres of the same hemp, had hold of segments of the rope at billions of points. And as if they were methodically tracing each segment to find more and more of a total pattern. And as if they were growing in the process. As if they had become the rope they had traced and would become the rope to be traced.

But until the rope-tracing was complete, Mr. Quattlebaum acknowledged, men would be reasoning imperfectly—with incomplete concepts, none frozen into an "isolated sameness," and many therefore meaning different things to different men in different contexts. "A logic that dispenses with the meanings of actual minds in settling the sense of its propositions is cutting its own root. *Words* are not true or false. Nor can we speak of *the* meaning of a verbal proposition as if it possessed one in its own right, apart from any investiture by thought. It is only as words are made the vehicle of meaning or asserted content that logic has any use for them. And this meaning, as asserted by actual minds, does clearly vary with its context."[2]

The larger the context, the larger the truth? The smaller the context, the smaller the truth?

What, Mr. Quattlebaum asked himself, was the largest possible context?

The total universe.

What was the largest possible truth?

The total universe—all concepts in all of their logically necessary interrelationships, deriving part of their very nature from such relationships—in the one and only complete context of logical congruity or coherence.

Was reason the criterion of total truth?

No. Reason, he said, was an activity of incomplete mind towards self-completion. Total truth was mind complete, and its own criterion: total logical context, unity, consistency, consonance, congruity, interdependence. Total logical *coherence.*

Could we say that total logical coherence was also *man's* criterion of truth?

Academically, yes; but only academically, Mr. Quattlebaum believed. If man's present knowledge were to be extended to completion, there was reason to believe it would identify with the total logical coherence of the universe. But if *total* coherence were man's working criterion, he could not test *any* hypothesis. For no man comprehended the total universe.

Could we say that logical coherence of and with his present knowledge was man's criterion of truth?

It seemed so to him. "For all the ordinary purposes of life, coherence does not mean coherence with some inaccessible absolute, but with the system of present knowledge."[3] And this "new" notion of the nature and test of truth was precisely the notion generally held and followed by men everywhere since and before the dawn of civilization. Reason alone was not our working criterion. Many relatively ungifted men had virtually stumbled onto truth which was truth because it cohered with the balance of human knowledge. And many brilliant men had reasoned beautifully within the contexts of plausible hypotheses which nevertheless had refused to cohere with the vastly larger context of the balance of man's knowledge.

Mr. Quattlebaum believed he had found, in logical coherence, a definition and criterion of truth upon which he could hang his hat. But there were a few friends who at first doubted that his hat rack was really that sturdy.

There was one jovial fellow, for instance, who repeatedly accused him of arguing in a circle. "Quat," he would say, "you're cheating. You're saying that truths *1, 2* and *3* are true because they cohere with truths *8, 9* and *10*, and that truths *8, 9* and *10* are true because they cohere with truths *1, 2* and *3*. You're saying that new truths are true because they cohere with old truths, and that old truths are true because they cohere with new truths."

Mr. Quattlebaum was saying no such thing. He was in fact denying that *any* truth possessed *independent* truth to "lend" to another. He was denying that there was any such thing as truth *1, 2, 3, 8, 9, 10*, a new truth, an old truth or any other truth *outside* a coherent context. " 'Coherence' cannot be attached to propositions from the outside: it is not a property which they can acquire by colligation, whilst retaining unaltered the truth they possessed in isolation."[4]

What was "true" of a stomach, liver or nervous system outside the context of an entire body? What was "true" of a body out-side the context of an environment? A coherent context was not one whose parts merely failed to contradict one another, but one whose parts actually stood in positive logical relationships of *entailment.*[5]

"Nor is there anything exceptional or mysterious in the concep-tion of mutual support. We cannot make one card stand up on end; but if we take two we may prop them against each other at an angle so that each prevents the other from falling."[6] "Thought is simply the spirit of totality within experience . . . There is no immediate experience in which we may remain standing; for every supposed immediate experience is linked with a context and harbors within itself the impulse to its own transcendence. This impulse is towards the system within which the immediate experience falls."[7]

Among other critics were "conservatives" who said coherence was a too-"liberal" criterion of truth, and "liberals" who said it was too "conservative."

"Conservatives" said it toppled truth from its throne and made truth only relative and changing rather than certain and permanent. If the total logical coherence of everything in the universe was the only completely true truth, then man, who did not yet fully com-prehend the total universe, could be certain of nothing. He could reach only partial truth, relative truth, degrees of truth. He could not even regard the fourness of two and two, or the "fact" that World War II ended in 1946, as absolutely true. Yesterday's truth could become today's falsehood. In fact, if a man could know truth only "in degree," how could any man say it was "absolutely true" that logical coherence was the criterion of truth?

Mr. Quattlebaum replied that, whatever truth was, it would re-main topple-proof—and that the coherence criterion therefore could topple, at most, nothing more than previously unexamined *notions* of truth, including his own.

Neither the coherence criterion nor Mr. Quattlebaum nor any-one else could "make" truth only relative or changing or degreed. At best, truth's characteristics could only be found. He had not set out to prove anything. He had only looked. And these were among the characteristics of truth which he believed he had found. Certainly he hadn't just *dreamed up* the apparent fact that his sassafras leaves were so dynamic—consisting of concepts logically interrelated with every other concept in the universe, hence partly beyond human experience, hence not *completely* true in isolation. "The plain man finds it hard to take seriously the contention that a motor accident in China has something to do with the weather in Philadelphia, or that the pleasure he takes in his own breakfast would be different if Genghis Khan had not, as an infant, had the croup. The theory seems preposterous on its face. (But) reflection often domesticates theories that to common sense are very wild, and in our own view the present theory is one of them."[8]

Yes, Mr. Quattlebaum acknowledged to his critics, he did accept the implication that human truth could be true only in degree, simply because it couldn't include any part of the truth which it couldn't include. "A given judgment is true in the *degree* to which its content could maintain itself in the light of a completed system of knowledge, false in the *degree* to which its appearance there would require its transformation."[9] And no man ever knew what that degree was today or what it would be tomorrow.

Yes, he acknowledged, human truth was partial, changing and impermanent. For its context broadened every day, and there was more context to come.

Yes, the fourness of two and two seemed "true;" but only in a context of numbers, outside which it was meaningless. And only on the unwarranted assumptions that the context of numbers was already complete and that a larger context, of which the context of numbers was only a part, could not affect the fourness of two and two.

Yes, it was "true only in degree" that World War II had ended in 1946. And such degree or degrees could be determined, Mr. Quattlebaum insisted, only by the extent to which *meanings* of those words were logically coherent with the balance of human knowledge. If they were jabbered mechanically by an idiot, the assertion would be true in very small degree. If they were spoken by a majority of able historians—familiar with the history of previ-

ous centuries and of the years which had followed 1946, familiar
with Versailles and with repeal of the U.S. neutrality law and with
the U.S. lend-lease law and with later events in Egypt, Israel, Cuba,
Laos, Vietnam, etc.—then the assertion could be true in very great
or small degree, dependent again upon what was *meant* by the
historians using the words, and upon the extent to which such
meaning cohered with the balance of human knowledge. "The degree of truth is measured by the degree of fullness of expression
which the significance obtains in each case. But though the significance pulsates through all the several judgments, it refuses to be
dissected into detached bits of meaning, or to be confined within
a single judgment taken in isolation. And in this sense no single
judgment possesses meaning or truth."[10]

No, Mr. Quattlebaum replied to his critics, his belief in degrees
of truth did not mean that yesterday's truth could become today's
falsehood. Rather it was his critics themselves who would be confronted by such a dilemma if human truth were the frozen, certain
thing which they thought they wanted it to be. Mr. Quattlebaum
believed himself unqualified to judge whether the astronomy and
geography of Ptolemy had been sufficiently coherent with the balance of human knowledge in the second century A.D. to warrant
their being called tentatively "true" by Ptolemy's contemporaries.
But he could imagine that such might have been the case. If Mr.
Quattlebaum's critics had been living then, some, he believed,
would have insisted upon the non-relative "absoluteness" of Ptolemy's "truths"— and, had such critics remained alive into the eras
of Copernicus, Newton, Einstein, etc., they would have had to
choose one or the other horn of a painful dilemma. They would
have had to admit either that yesterday's truth *had* become today's
absolute and obsolete falsehood or that the coherent context did
make a difference—*all* the difference—in what man might properly
regard as tentatively "true" at any given point in history.

It was not one day's truth which became the next day's falsehood,
Mr. Quattlebaum insisted. Truth (part of it beyond human experience) remained the same. It was human *knowledge* of truth which
changed, grew and thus provided an ever-expanding context in

which those assertions which cohered with it might properly be called tentatively true. Only "tentatively," he again pointed out, because none of today's "truths" properly could be granted dispensation from further tests in the contexts of all the tomorrows.

And so, yes, he contentedly confessed to these "conservative" critics, even logical coherence itself must remain an only tentatively true test of truth. Under his own criterion, he could not "absolutely" *know* his own criterion to be "absolutely" true. He believed that, in the absence of human omniscience, no intellectually honest man could assert more than the partial truth of any proposition—for no human proposition, outside the context of a total universe not yet comprehended by any man, could itself be more than partially comprehended. He "knew" only that the theory of coherence as the criterion of truth seemed *itself* to cohere with everything he now "knew." And it seemed to him a strong but gentle hypothesis. He felt well vaccinated by it—against rashness and bigotry, against presumptions and pomposities. "While supporting the belief in scientific advance, it refuses to believe that this advance has reached the end of the road. It is absolutistic without dogmatism, and relativistic without countenancing despair."[11]

"Liberal" critics, on the other hand, noting that some assertions could be "coherent and still not true," asked whether his views might not help to entrench "ultra-conservatism" and even to encourage some of the crotchety cranks who thrived on "paranoidal system-building."

Naturally, Mr. Quattlebaum reacted rather sharply to this sort of thing. But, to coin a phrase, he was "glad they had raised these questions"—not only because he felt it was important and easy to answer them, but also because they gave him an opportunity to italicize a few points to which he wished to give added emphasis.

In essence these "liberal" critics were saying that some persons, organizations, manufacturers, news media, political parties, governments and churches, for example, had built up, through the years, bodies of policy, creed or dogma in which they held an increasingly vested interest. Each was a "coherent context" in which to "test" anything new that might claim to be true, and with which to rationalize, not infrequently, the calling of new truth false and the keeping of new truth out. Even if unwittingly, was not Mr. Quattlebaum's view lending added sanction and sanctuary to such attitudes and practices?

"Oh, hell, no," Mr. Quattlebaum was heard to reply. "That's exactly what it does *not* do. Its every implication cries out clear and loud for the testing of the truth of every proposition by its coherence with *total* human knowledge, not by its relatively meaningless coherence with any mere fragment of human knowledge conveniently arranged and fortified to serve the sick or selfish purposes of any person, group, government or church.

"Of course there can be coherence without appreciable truth," he acknowledged. "We all have coherent dreams, for example. We all know of unfortunate psychotics with too much coherence within too little context. We all have friends who delight in mixing a measure of 'proven fact' with a measure of imagination and coming up with half-baked but 'coherent proofs' that all the world's ills are due to specific little bands of unspecified conspirators. We all know 'fundamental Americans' who clutch flags to their breasts and deny the rights of Negroes 'because' such denial can be 'made to cohere' with the fact that George Washington and Thomas Jefferson had slaves two centuries ago. We all know men who assert the truth of propositions 'because' they 'cohere' with a humanly fallible pronouncement of infallibility.

"But these are all instances of coherence with mere fragments of total human knowledge," Mr. Quattlebaum emphasized, "whereas it is coherence with *total* human knowledge which our thesis holds to be man's proper criterion of truth. Where is there another thesis which seems so made-to-order for the responsible 'liberal,' which so fundamentally challenges the right of limited context to shape men's views of truth, which so insists that the *whole* of human knowledge is the context-to-be-cohered-with, and which so flatly disputes the validity of the double standard? It is central to this thesis that there is only one universe, only one coherent whole, only one totality of human knowledge. There cannot be two or more, or none would be total. If there were two, each would differ from the other if only in the respect in which each was not the other, thus disputing the right of either to call itself complete.

"Now please tell *me* something," Mr. Quattlebaum asked his "liberal" critics. "In your commendable efforts to discard dirty old bath water, haven't you slackened your precautions against discarding the baby? Into more and more of your otherwise valid criticisms of particular 'systems of thought,' has there not crept an alarming number of ill-considered, overly generalized and disturbingly presumptuous slurs upon the very *concepts* of 'thought system,' 'systematic thought' and 'system' *per se?*

"Can't you do battle against specific 'systems of thought' which are unfounded, ungrounded, incompetent, distorted, rationalized, apologetic, self-serving, unrealistic, outmoded or arbitrarily contrived—without naïvely and recklessly demanding that 'system itself' be sacrificed pointlessly as an innocent victim? Can't you prune dead wood, fight tree disease and remove 'wolf' trees without setting fire to the whole forest?

"Are you *real* 'liberals'—the kind who would rebel against attempts to confine human thought within the conclusions of an Italian theologian who drew heavily, seven centuries ago, upon conclusions reached by a Greek philosopher twenty-two centuries ago? Or are you dilettantes—the kind who could prattle that a goose-stepping militarism was the natural progeny of an Hegelian 'thought system'?

"Oppose *a* system or *the* system, if you will, when and for whatever good reason it may deserve logical opposition. But why be drawn into naïve opposition to *system*, the very *concept* of essential principles or facts in a rational dependence or connection —a coherent whole? Can one define or even conceive an *un*-'systematic' astronomy, biology, chemistry, demography, geology, mathematics, physics, football strategy or philosophy? Is not 'systematized knowledge' the very definition of science?"

While pulling off his socks one night, Mr. Quattlebaum recalled his examination, months before, of the "credentials" of purported tests of truth. He then had rejected self-evidence, faith, "authority," pragmatism, intuition and "correspondence."[12] And, while refraining from premature judgment as to whether there was such a thing as a "real mystic" capable of massive intuitional insights into truth, he had concluded that alleged mystic experience could not be a dependable source or test of truth for any of the *non*-mystics who, as Dr. Reasner had observed, seemed to constitute the bulk of mankind.[13]

Had he been too hasty? Might logical coherence be no more than an overly complex synonym for self-evidence, for example? Or for faith or "authority"? Or for whatever "worked" for the pragmatist? Or for intuition? Or for whatever might "correspond" to the total context of the universe? Or for the "ordered totality" of a mystic's insight?

On the contrary, it now seemed to Mr. Quattlebaum quite clear that it was not a case of logical coherence being an over-complex synonym for any of these purported tests of truth; rather *they* had become the over-simplified shorthand synonyms for logical coherence.

To assert the self-evidence of an "absolute truth," for example, was to assert its truth apart from its relationships with *any*thing else —whereas, as Mr. Quattlebaum noted again, he had been led to the criterion of logical coherence precisely because he had found it impossible to assert the truth or existence of anything apart from its relationships with *every*thing else. A "truth" described as "completely self-evident" was one which seemed to cohere with total human knowledge, and whose denial would leave *nothing* coherent —not even the fourness of two and two. A truth with a higher *degree* of self-evidence than another was one which seemed to cohere with more of human knowledge than did the other, and whose denial would contradict a greater portion of total human knowledge.

As a criterion of truth, it was not coherence which could be resolved into self-evidence, but self-evidence which derived its plausibility from the more fundamental criterion of logical coherence.

By the same token, Mr. Quattlebaum observed, those things in which most men seemed to profess most faith, those pronouncements by "authorities" to which most men seemed to pledge most allegiance, those practices and beliefs which seemed to "work" most consistently for most pragmatists and those intuitions which seemed to afford most dependable insights were, for the most part, ones which seemed most coherent with the whole of human knowledge.

Nor could such logical coherence be reduced in any instance to mere "correspondence" with anything else. For, just as man's exclusively mental experience could include no exclusively "physical" thing to correspond with any of his mental perceptions, so there could be no *total* human knowledge with which any *partial* truth could correspond, nor any total truth (beyond human experience) with which humanly experienced truth could be seen to correspond.

And the "mystic"? Mr. Quattlebaum still could not know whether such a person existed; for he was not aware that he himself was a mystic, and obviously no self-professed mystic could communicate to him or to anyone else the content of any experience which by definition was incommunicable. But he had concluded that "all objects belong to some knower,"[14] and he knew that self-professed mystics believed that "the objects and the knowers belong to each other—they are the same . . . they are one,"[15] and he believed that this could provide meaningful sanction for William James' conviction that the potentiality of mystical insight was within all men.[16] So he *could* believe that some men might have such insights into the truth or truths of a whole of which they themselves were quite literal parts, but such belief was not incumbent upon him. So he merely deferred judgment—confident that any truth experienced by a mystic could be truth only because it cohered logically with, or indeed *was*, "real" truth itself, but equally confident that no impossible "report" from an alleged mystic properly could be considered, by himself or by anyone else, mystic or non-mystic, as a valid *criterion* of truth.

As a criterion of truth, logical coherence seemed irreducible to any other; and every other seemed reducible to logical coherence.

It seemed to Mr. Quattlebaum that he had found how and where and why to hang his hat.

28. The Wholly Spirit

"I do hope you've left room for god," said Gertrude.

"To 'leave room' for anything," Mr. Quattlebaum replied, "is to cheat. I have tried merely to observe."

Gert. And you observe a world without matter, a world full of mind?

Quat. It seems to be a conscious universe—one in which no one ever has experienced, or can experience, any "physical" thing "out there in space and time." Experience is conscious. And one simply cannot experience what one cannot experience. The universe appears to be the total field of consciousness, in which all men and things are groups of logically interrelated mental concepts—and thus sub-fields of consciousness, overlapped and intertwined. Each man and each thing seems an indispensably necessary component of the one, complete, coherent mental context which appears to constitute total, logically necessary fact and truth.

Gert. And surely, Quat, you believe that such a universe must have been created by an omnipotent god?

Quat. Not in any conventional sense. Surely not "out of nothing." Omnipotence is a poor synonym for irrationality or black magic. As the world matures, it discards its wishfully obsessive pretense that an "omnipotent" god can create temples without stone, paintings without oils, symphonies without notes, or sand castles without shovel or pail on a sandless beach.

Gert. Then where did it all come from? And when?

Quat. Beyond a total universe—containing all concepts, including those of space and time—there could be no "whereness," "whenness" or anything else. A total universe could not be created by something outside a total universe, for the very separateness of a total universe from its "creator" would make a total universe not total at all. And if, by virtue of being total, a total universe contained all space and time, there could be no residual space or time, outside the universe, in which such a creative act could occur.

Gert. Yes, but . . .

Quat. Hear me out. What do we mean by a "creative" act? An instance of cause-and-effect? But we earlier rejected the naïve notion that cause-and-effect was mere "brute event." We agreed that instances of cause-and-effect, and hence of creation, were instances of logical relationship between certain mental concepts.[1] If all such concepts are within the universe—if space and time are on its *in*side rather than on its *out*side, so to speak—then the universe is literally eternal. It didn't "begin." It can't "end." It just "is"—*per omnia saecula saeculorum*—"as it was in the beginning, is now and ever shall be, world without end."[2]

Gert. Then you find no god?

Quat. I believe I *have* found god. Not a puny, pretended "creator" dangling impossibly beyond the universe. Nor an endlessly rationalized "creature" of fearful fantasies piously contrived "that the prophesies might be fulfilled." And certainly not a bearded father-giant carried on a throne through streets of golden brick. But damned if I don't believe I may have found an inescapably *real* god. One I can understand and believe. One I can wish and try to serve. Whose only throne may be a chair at the kitchen table. Whose blood may flow in every vein, in intimate communion with every man and with every leaf of every tree throughout the universe. Whose very being in fact may *be* that communion. May *be* that universe.

Gert. Not once, Quat, in all these months, did you ever indicate to me that you were thinking about god at all.

Quat. I wasn't. I was looking only for a definition of truth. But the only one upon which I now can hang my hat embraces some of those very characteristics—and brings to mind some of those very adjectives, synonyms and metaphors—with which men long have sought to define, describe, denote or connote "god." If total truth is the total universe in total logical coherence (with all its components, including space and time, interrelated in logically necessary interdependence),[3] then *where else* would man find "supreme being," "supreme truth," "eternity," "omniscience," "omnipotence," or the "self-existent," "all-wise," "all-just," "all-righteous," "all-sustaining" or "almighty"? Where else would he find a "natural law" or a "god's will" comprehensible within the dignity of human reason? And where else would he find supreme "understanding," "benevolence," "compassion," "kindness," "love" and "mercy"—if not in the totality of a universe, or god, which could not *be* total, or god, if a single person or thing or relationship were missing from its total context—or if each such person, thing and relationship were not precisely what it is *because of* that total context? Gert, if god is the name of the universe, god now *means* something to me.

Gert. You are saying, then, that the universe, as it appears to you, actually *is* god? And that you and I, as parts of the universe, also are literally parts of god?

Quat. You and I and everyone and everything around us: atheists, pagans, agnostics, Unitarians, Catholics, Christian Scientists, Jews, muskrats, sassafras trees, hereness and my fishing flies. I now see a *respect in which* the fellows who put together the first part of Genesis could be right in asserting that man *and* his environment are in god's own image, "in the likeness of ourselves . . . in the image of himself."[4] I agree with Paul, the Roman-Jewish tent-maker who joined the Christians after stoning them, that "just as each of our bodies has several parts and each part has a separate function, so all of us, in union with (god), form one body, and as parts of it we belong to each other."[5]

Gert. You are quoting from the Bible?

Quat. Not as a proof, of course—and perhaps, but perhaps not, a bit out of context. But isn't it at least interesting to note the apparent consonance of such old passages with a notion that, as parts of the universe, we also are parts of god?

Gert. Are you thinking, for example, of such phrases as "heaven *and earth* are full of your glory"?[6] And of the prayer that the "will" of god—or of the universe, if you prefer—"be done *on earth* as in heaven"?[7]

Quat. Yes, but even more about some of the things which Paul and John apparently said. To the few Athenians who would listen to him, Paul said in about 51 A.D. that "god . . .the one whom you already worship without knowing it . . . does not make his home in shrines" and that "the whole human race," comprised of "one single stock . . . might seek the deity and, by feeling their way towards him, succeed in finding him . . . in fact he is not far away from any of us, since it is *in* him that we live, and move, and *exist*, as indeed some of your own writers have said."[8]

Gert. But Paul chose those words for Greeks, with many of whom such phrases and thoughts were traditional.

Quat. Precisely. Not being in Rome, he chose not to speak as Romans spoke. But was he burned for heresy?

Gert. Not that I recall.

Quat. And I find it interesting that the central concept of Christianity is incarnation—god as a man and man as a god: "one god" and at least one man who was "of one substance with (god) . . . incarnate."[9] John said, "In the beginning was the Word (or "Wisdom, present with God before the world"): the Word (or "Wisdom," or total truth) was *with* God and the Word (or "Wisdom," or total truth) *was* God . . . not one thing had its being but *through* him. *All* that came to be had life *in* him and that life was the light of men . . . . The Word (or "Wisdom") was the true light that enlightens all men . . . in the world that had its being *through* him . . . He came to his own domain . . . The Word (or "Wisdom") was made *(man)*, he lived among us, and we saw his glory, the glory that is his as the . . . . Son of the Father, full of . . . *truth*."[10]

Gert. To say that one man was god incarnate is not to say that all men are god incarnate.

Quat. But to say that god *is* the universe is to say that we are *parts* of god, and that wheat, wine and everything else *already* are god's "body and blood"—with or without the "mysterious" alchemy of liturgical "consecration." What is the real marvel of incarnation? That a "spiritual" god slipped into the "material" body of *one* man, alleged to have been as omniscient and complete as god, and hence god in fact? Or that *all* men and environments are as exclusively "spiritual" as is god, and that all are god's parts, and that all are moving toward identification with that same complete and omniscient context?

Gert. Are you a pantheist?

Quat. Oh, *damn* that word!

Gert. But are you?

Quat. In a most unconventional sense.

Gert. Are you a heretic?

Quat. And damn *that* word. A heresy is an opinion held by a man who, in the opinion of a second, is not in accord with a third. And the world is full of orthodox heresy and heretical orthodoxy. Pantheism is called heresy by those who assume that the world is both material and spiritual, both natural and supernatural. They find it difficult, as would I, to picture *spirit* floating around within *material* stones or sticks or mountain brooks. It isn't easy to envisage heavenly vapors wafting between darting atoms or through bloody bones and chromosomes. Yet these question-beggars seem incredibly unaware of the similar trap into which they are pulled by their same assumptions. They assume that their world is comprised of two distinct "substances," spirit and matter (so distinct as to escape any possibility of equation). Yet they also assume that spirit and matter are *not* so distinct as to escape interaction or communication with each other. There are, for example, many assumptions that a godly "spirit" interacts with a "material" man (or with a "spiritual soul" somehow contained within a "material" man). But there are few attempts to explain how. And to me, as you know, these few attempts (as by Descartes, for instance) have seemed pathetic failures.[11]

Gert. Obviously, then, you could be called a pantheist only, as you put it, "in a most unconventional sense"—simply because conventional pantheism has assumed a dualistic universe of spirit and matter, while you believe it is wholly spirit. For you, logical interaction is the very nature of mental concepts, or spirit; and you are not even confronted with the problem of how spirit could interact with a matter for which you find no evidence. Your own "pantheism," then, if I may use that "damned word" again, is indeed a quite different thing—and only a by-product or implication of your other observations.

Quat. Exactly. And, whether you call it pantheism or immanence, the indwelling presence of a god in man and in his environment is by no means foreign to Christian trinity (god, man and spirit), to Unitarian unity, to the all-mind-and-no-matter of the Christian Scientist, or to comparable concepts in many other religious and non-religious contexts. The "Christian (and much non-Christian) . . . emphasis on immanence . . . is not nearly enough realized."[12]

Gert. Are there other arguments against pantheism or immanence?

Quat. Yes, but again each is based upon assumed premises which seem unable to withstand scrutiny. When Pius IX complained that to call the universe god was to call god changeable,[13] he assumed a changeable universe, which I cannot;[14] I find change only in our necessarily partial *glimpses* of a universe which, in its entirety, I find as necessarily unchangeable as he believed god to be, and as I too believe god to be. Other arguments rest upon vague notions of time. With a man who objects that a god-universe "attains its fulness only by a process of *evolution* or 'becoming,' the stages of which form the history of the universe,"[15] and with the earlier Vatican Council which denied that "all things *evolve* from god's essence,"[16] and with a Pius IX who said god does not *become* god in man in the world,[17] I quite agree. But for a quite different reason. They assumed the universe to be within time; I believe time to be within the universe. And so I view evolution not as a chronologically vacuum-filling process, but rather as relationships between the concepts (including the concept of time) which timelessly *constitute* the universe—which I also call god.

Gert. It also has been argued that what you call god can act only out of necessity and hence that neither such a god, nor any man who is a part of such a god, can be called either good or evil.[18] But I believe you dealt with this earlier.

Quat. Yes. This argument unfairly assumes the very thing it asserts: that there is a kind of necessity beyond god to which god is therefore subject, whereas I feel compelled to believe, as you know, that it is the total context of the universe—or god—which itself *constitutes* all logical necessity. The argument also resorts to the traditional notion of a "free will" which we could not substantiate.[19]

Gert. Some may complain that your concept of god makes individual immortality meaningless because all "souls" or selves, "good" or "bad," are absorbed or merged into total consciousness and thus "treated" indiscriminately.[20]

Quat. Oh, I suppose some will see old Quattlebaum's god as a mop sopping up souls. But they will be doubly mistaken. They will have reverted to the naïve notion of consciousness or spirit as a vapid, airy, homogeneous "substance," capable somehow of "containing" isolated thoughts, virtues, values and the like.[21] And they will have forgot that, unless every man already is a part of the total universe, there *is* no total universe! Selves cannot be added, like cups of pure water or sewage, to the sea of totality—indiscriminately or otherwise; for unless they already are in that sea, it is not total. If the total conscious universe is god, there can be, outside that totality, no residue of selves remaining to be absorbed.[22] Why are you frowning?

Gert. Am I? I suppose I was trying to imagine how Alice and Ev would react to all this. Would it seem human and personal enough? Is anything more personal, after all, than one's own awareness and reverence and love of god? Than one's own devotion and service to god? Than one's own adoration of god?

Quat. But what sort of god? Can we really revere or love or serve or adore something we can't define?

Gert. People do. *I* do.

Quat. Not really. You don't worship or pray to *nothing*. You have a god of *some* kind in mind. So you have at least a partial or hypothetical definition. And none of us is capable of more than that. But may we not—and should we not—make more use of our admittedly limited capabilities to sharpen up the hypothetical definitions of god which we have left relatively unexamined for so many years? Let's face the fact that for most of us god has been a mail-order bride. Her agents, letters and snapshots have created in our minds a vast variety of images, impressions, anticipations, apprehensions, fears or wishful thinking. If and when she should arrive in person, all of us would experience *some* surprises, for better or worse, no matter what. She wouldn't be exactly what *any* of us had pictured. Not because she had changed, but because we had not exhaustively researched her in advance.

Gert. But who can exhaustively research god?

Quat. No one. But *some* research is possible. A man ought to know more than weight, height and color of hair before closing a deal on a mail-order bride. Maybe she's a prostitute. Maybe she has syphilis. Some of our notions of god are comparably shot through with unanalyzed attributes and abstractions and already demonstrable errors. Certainly *this* is a valid and possible area for research. And if some of the results call for major overhauls of some notions of god, wouldn't you and Alice and Ev and most other persons want to know about it?

Gert. Yes, but what I asked was whether your particular notion of god would seem *personal* enough for Alice and Ev. Wouldn't it be a major departure for anyone accustomed to thinking in terms of a relationship between a personal god and his own personal self?

Quat. On the contrary, I no longer see such a person-to-person relationship as merely possible but rather as essential and inevitable. Having found no such thing as an isolated self, I came to regard selves as partially identifying, "overlapping," growing parts of a conscious universe,[23] and to view their total as *all* person. As the whole person. As god. The god-to-man and man-to-god relationship thus becomes much *more* personal than any imagined relationship between two wholly separate selves. For god is not apart from man, but rather the total of men and of their environments. Their total is god. No relationship could be more personal or more intimately so. It cannot be god's lack of personality (of which god appears to be the literal total), but only our inadequately formed notions of such personality, which could permit such a concept of god to seem at all impersonal.

Gert. These personal relationships—are they between virtuous men and a sinful god?

Quat. I'm missing your point.

Gert. Well, if god is the total universe, and if the universe contains sin and error, doesn't it follow that sin and error exist within god? Or, if sin and error are not parts of god, how could they exist within men—whom you call parts of god?

Quat. When we believe that something conforms to truth, we call it moral, good, just or right. A sin or error is a transgression or absence of truth. But what is truth? I see complete truth as the one logically necessary coherence of all the interrelated mental concepts which constitute the total universe—the total context[24]—which I also call god. But because vast parts of that total context obviously are still beyond man's experience, I see man's *working* criterion of truth as "logical coherence of and with his present knowledge,"[25] which consists of ever-expanding sub-contexts of still incomplete concepts within the total. As man's sub-contexts of knowledge expand, as he comes to see more and more of "the whole picture," there are quite valid changes in his judgments about truth. In smaller sub-contexts, at earlier stages, he regards as wrong or sinful—or as virtuous or non-sinful—certain practices about which, in larger sub-contexts at later stages, he validly changes his mind.

Gert. Such as?

Quat. Such as usury, slavery and birth control. Such as Ptolemy's astronomy and geography. Such as selfish "personal salvation" *outside* "the world" as against unselfish service to others *in* "the world." Such as a Roman Catholic's non-consumption in one era, and consumption in another era, of meat on Friday or of any food or drink after a midnight before "communion."

Gert. So what is wrong or sinful in one context may not be wrong or sinful in a larger context, because the truth which is transgressed in the prior context may no longer be true in the later and larger context. Is that what you mean?

Quat. Not quite. What changes is not truth itself but only man's knowledge of it. What a man calls wrong or sinful in one context he may not call wrong or sinful in a larger context, because his knowledge of a "truth" which was allegedly transgressed in a prior context may become a larger knowledge of truth in a later and larger context. And the one and only *total* truth, the only total context, the only coherence of *all* mental concepts in their one and only complete set of logically necessary interrelationships, can be transgressed by men, knowingly or unknowingly, but could not transgress itself without ceasing to *be* itself. So within this one and only completely ordered totality, or god, there can be no wrong or sin.

Gert. Yet there can be wrong or sin in men, who you say are parts of god.

Quat. Yes, but not despite the fact that we are parts of *god*, but rather because we are only *parts*. The only relatively well-ordered and still incomplete concepts of which we and our environments are comprised, as sub-contexts of the whole, are fully ordered and complete only in the total context. Error can exist only within, and by virtue of being, *fragments* of truth. Components of error in a sub-context become components of truth in the total context. Even erroneous premises of a syllogism can yield a true conclusion.

Gert. For example?

Quat. Every alligator has become President of the United States. False. Franklin D. Roosevelt was an alligator. False. Therefore Franklin D. Roosevelt became President of the United States. True.

Gert. You know, Quat, I've actually come to have a warm and gentle sort of feeling about all this business of coherence-in-context as the nature and test of truth. About god in man's world and man in god's. About man in the kingdom of god and god as that kingdom. About man and his knowledge and his errors and his goodness as being "profane" perhaps only in the sense that they are not yet fulfilled. And perhaps touching and touched by the "divine" in the sense that they are at least parts of the total context. And that whatever is profane may be no less the profanity of god. Of course, I'm not nearly as qualified as others to *know* about any of these things, but . . .

Quat. Nor I, dear. Implied within the entire hypothesis is the fact that it can be *no more than* hypothesis, and that growing coherence within growing contexts may prove itself less than it seems.

Gert. Yet I must say—perhaps it's the woman in me—that somehow it all *feels* so right. In the deepest of what I call my own religious experience, and in love itself, I seem to find the same sort of de-emphasis of an isolated personality, this greater emphasis upon service to others. This lessening concern for "my own personal rights." This merging or interrelatedness or partly *identifying* with others and with god. This sense of humility before a vast and vastly understanding god. And yet this sense of possessing some small but real dignity and worth. This feeling that god may want and need me as I want and need god.

Quat. I find it that way. It has seemed to breed some brotherhood into, and some bigotry out of, my own whole view of men and things. It has seemed to leave me more compassionate and tolerant of others, more charitable and understanding. It has seemed to relieve the psychological conflict that comes with the unqualified defense of "absolutes"—which now seem humanly provable or disprovable only in degree, and fair game for any honest scrutiny.

Gert. And if god as total universe depends upon its total context to be god—and if each part of that context depends upon god, as that total, to be what *it* is—perhaps we may have a clearer understanding of what it may mean "to create." One synonym is "to constitute." Another is "to produce as a work of thought." And perhaps "creative" work in the arts or sciences, the burning of wood and the measuring of its ashes and gases, or the bearing of a child in the "creation" of "new" life, is not to make something all-new or anything out of nothing, but to serve as a medium through which concepts are rearranged in new contexts—through which concepts and contexts, previously existing but beyond man's previous experience, are uncovered to human view. In such a sense we may seem to glimpse a sort of timeless *constancy* of "creation" by a god that is total context. Perhaps in the beginning was tomorrow. Want some coffee?

Quat. I'd prefer beer, thanks—a cold cluster of my favorite liquid concepts: tanginess, amberness, frothness, maltness, hopsness, slakeness, quenchness, glowness . . .

Gert. Not another litany, please.

Quat. A farewell toast. A fond and firm farewell to false dichotomies. Farewell to the material versus the mental. Farewell to faith versus reason. To orthodoxy versus heresy. To the spiritual versus the secular. To the supernatural versus the natural. To the sacred versus the profane.

Gert. That much melodrama on half a glass of beer? Don't you want to add "all hail the ecumenical!"?

Quat. That would depend.

Gert. Upon what? Who is more ecumenically disposed than you?

Quat. Probably no one.

Gert. Then why do you hesitate?

Quat. The word comes from the Greek *oikoumenikos:* "the *(entire)* inhabited world." It means universal. But its secondary meaning—only "religiously" universal rather than universally universal—remains the more popular connotation. Assumptions that religious truth is something mysteriously set apart from other truth are still too much with us. Another toast. To one truth—total, undivided and unperverted—not for an inhibited world, but for the inhabited world.

Gert. I'll drink to that. But I hope you are still pleased that so many churches have begun to prune away at least some of their dead limbs.

Quat. Very pleased. But still impatient.

Gert. Surgery, including tree surgery, should not be recklessly fast.

Quat. Nor fatally unprompt. Nor just to make the patient *look* better. Nor should there be any surgery at all before thorough and conclusive diagnosis or X-rays. And my chief concern is that even some of the more honest of churches—those which really *do* want to "get well"—may not be looking in the right places for the real sources and causes of their diseases or conflicts.

Gert. Where are they looking and not looking?

Quat. They seem to be looking more at their leaves than at their trunks or roots or seeds. In genial gestures of new good will, churches are permitting and even encouraging their leaves to brush against and among those of others, in an increasingly pleasant and harmonious inter-rustling of "dialogue." But they may be exchanging more bugs and worms than truth. For the leaves are only theological *super*structures, stemming from and towering far beyond the main trunks and *root* structures of philosophical conclusions or assumptions. And philosophy is more basic than theology.[26]

Gert. So, while you are happy to see polemical theology being replaced by an irenical theology, which seeks less strife and more unity, you feel that this is still not the answer?

Quat. Certainly not. When ten theologians decide to stop fighting and engage in a common search for theological conclusions upon which they can agree, this is good. But what is ironic about the irenic is that they may reach agreement upon so many conclusions which may still be wrong. If all ten proceed upon the basis of philosophically unexamined presumptions (that man has a quite separate body and soul, for example, or that there is a supernatural apart from a natural, or that the universe resides within time, or that "free will" is obvious), then they will merely have begged most of the questions underlying all the points on their agenda. They will have picked apart the crumbs of a single slice of bread—and starved to death while sitting upon unopened crates of food.

Gert. But there is less and less of this?

Quat. It seems to be on the decline. Just how steeply I really don't know.

Gert. But you are still optimistic?

Quat. I really am. For ultimately there is no alternative. The narrower and shallower streams of theological ecumenism have no place to flow but down from the sheltered hills and over the dams and out into the broad, deep sea of philosophical ecumenism—for *all* of our *oikoumenikos.* For I do *not* find "religious experience" to be a walled-off "specific kind of experience, but rather a certain organization of the whole of life"[27]—"the summed up meaning and purport of our whole consciousness of things . . . the expression of our ultimate attitude to the universe."[28]

Gert. Have you read this article?

Quat. Not yet. I was looking for it last night.

Gert. It was in the boys' bathroom. Would you like to hear what one of them underlined?

Quat. Very much.

Gert. Morris West is recalling a walk with a Buddhist monk in a monastery garden in Bangkok. He says he felt they were "at one . . . following different paths to a common end" expressed "in contradictory words." He says he "thought afterward of the history of heresy hunts and inquisitions and extorted confessions of faith . . . of six million dead in the gas chambers of Europe, and how long it took us to root out anti-Semitism, even from the liturgy of the Church. No wonder," he says, that "the salt lost its savor—when it was rubbed into the wounds of so many!" And "we are not foolish enough to imagine that the action of the Spirit is limited only to this battered (Church). We need . . . to look at it from the outside, to see how it appears to the men and women on the further mountains, to know whether it is, for them . . . a City of Witness or a grim fortress of ancient prejudice." He says "we were fanatics when we should have been simple seekers for the ground of union between men . . . We still repeat these historic sins . . . All over the world . . . there is a . . . revolt of the young . . . against beliefs imposed by authority, against cant and hypocrisy and double standards . . . against censorship and suppression . . . High words will not answer the songs of protest that they sing. Old-fashioned revivalism is no answer to the doubts that plague them. Threats will not coerce them . . . We must be rigidly and absolutely honest with them . . . and strip away the protective coverings we wear—the illusions . . . half-truths . . . formalisms . . . comforting rituals, the superstitions we have turned into dogmas . . . We cannot hedge a single point with them. We cannot dodge a single issue . . . the nature of faith, the roots of authority, freedom of conscience . . .

racism . . . And from this bleak moment of love, a new journey
begins: a fraternal search for a meaning, a walk back to the limits
of reason . . ."²⁹

Quat. Well?

Gert. You really do believe "the holy" is "in the common,"³⁰
don't you, Quat?

Quat. I have found no difference. Nor a man who has.

29. *Ad Hominem*

Dear Doc,

Here in your deserted office (your nurse says you've slipped away
to bother the bass at Wawakeechee), I'm leaving the stuff you
wanted to borrow—mostly quotations from some of the fellows
who have "thought some of my thoughts" in various ways and
degrees since 640 B.C.:

Thales, Anaximander, Anaximenes, Pythagoras, Xenophanes,
Heraclitus, Parmenides, Zeno, Gorgias, Melissus, Empedocles,
Anaxagoras, Democritus, Socrates, Plato, Aristotle, the second
Zeno, Cleanthes, Chrysippus, Poseidonius, Cicero, Philo, Galen,
Ammonius Saccas, Origen, Plotinus, Porphyry, Augustine, Boe-
thius, Johannes Scotus Erigena, al-Kindi, al-Farabi, Saadia, Avi-
cenna, Berengarius, Anselm, Abélard, Gilbert de la Porrée, Peter
Lombard, Averroës, Alan of Lille, Maimonides, Amalric of Bena,
Alexander of Hales, Albertus Magnus, Bonaventure, Matthew of
Aquasparta, Thomas Aquinas, Roger Bacon, Duns Scotus, Siger of
Brabant, Henry of Ghent, Johannes Eckhart, William of Occam,
Gemistus Pletho, Nicolaus Cusanus, Johannes Bessarion, Marsilio
Ficino, Judah ben Isaac, Bernardino Telesio, Giordano Bruno,
Tommaso Campanella, Descartes, Whichcote, Spinoza, Régis,

Malebranche, Leibniz, Berkeley, Kant, Fichte, Hegel, Schelling, Comte, Gioberti, Fechner, Newman, Lotze, Marx, Renan, T. H. Green, Mach, Bosanquet, Bradley, Royce, Croce, Gandhi, Russell, Marcel, Sartre, Camus, Teilhard, Lonergan . . .

Teilhard, for example, held that "matter and spirit . . . are not two separate substances,"[1] and that "it is in no way metaphorical" to say so.[2] Consciousness is "co-extensive with the universe," the universe is "thought,"[3] and only in "thought" are found the "properties attributed (usually) to matter."[4] The universe is the whole "soul . . . of which we are . . . a part."[5] We are "living the experience of a universe . . . gathered up . . . in each one of us."[6] Each "ego . . . makes everything else itself."[7] And "no fact . . . exists in pure isolation,"[8] but only in the "*coherence* of all that exists"[9]— a "plurality of individual reflections . . . reinforcing one another in the act of a single unanimous reflection,"[10] with "the world . . . giving '*immediacy*' to the divine, and the divine *spiritualizing* the tangible."[11] Yes, "a very real 'pantheism' . . . but . . . legitimate."[12] For "immortality of the soul . . . ceases to appear as anthropomorphic" and appears "in the (very) structure of the world."[13] And "religion and science are the two conjugated faces . . . of one and the same act of complete knowledge."[14] Teilhard, "reckoned . . . among the orthodox, and yet feeling with the heterodox," was "a link between the two."[15] For "religion is still, in its most living profundities, unknown to (many) men who claim to have examined all religious revelations;"[16] and an "awakening of (human) consciousness to (total) consciousness is . . . necessary if man is (to fuse) a passionate desire to conquer the world (with) a passionate desire to unite . . . with God."[17]

And for Lonergan what is "real" is not the "already out there now," but "the verifiable"[18]—within the "rational self-consciousness" that *comprises* god and man[19] and thus provides the "spontaneous inter-subjectivity" which, as the very "basis of their community," makes men social.[20] *Fundamentally* social. Mere "good will" is not enough. Unless employed in behalf of what is intelligent and reasonable, "good will" often imposes even "further evils on the already weary shoulders of mankind."[21] Hence Lonergan's "campaign against the flight from understanding," the flight that always leaves "superficial minds with superficial positions."[22] No, "the business of the human mind" is not smug "contemplation of what we (assume we) know, but relentless devotion to the task of adding increments to (an otherwise) merely habitual knowledge."[23] For "to exclude *(any)* insight is also to exclude the further questions that would arise from it and the complementary insights that would carry it toward a rounded and balanced viewpoint. To lack that fuller view results in behaviour that generates misunderstanding both in ourselves and in others. To suffer such incomprehension favours a withdrawal from the outer drama of human living into . . . phantasy."[24]

And so on.

No, Doc, the piling up of "supportive" quotations from these and the hundred other men cannot add automatically to the validity of my "case." But please do return them as soon as you can, because . . .

Well, maybe Gert or the kids or some of our friends will be interested to find that, within virtually every hour of the past twenty-six centuries, one or another of my eccentricities has been championed by at least one living man.

Quat

NOTES

Chapter 12

1. W. K. Clifford, "The Ethics of Belief," *Lectures and Essays* (London: Macmillan & Co., 1879), p. 186.

Chapter 13

1. William Pepperell Montague, *The Ways of Knowing* (London: George Allen & Unwin; New York: Macmillan Co., 1925), p. 44.
2. "From an address by the [Roman Catholic] Bishop of Newport, reported in *The Tablet* for August 27, 1904," as quoted by Durant Drake, *Invitation to Philosophy* (Boston: Houghton Mifflin Co., 1933), p. 5.
3. Samuel Taylor Coleridge, *Aids to Reflection* (London: Edward Moxon, 1854).
4. Robert McAfee Brown, "Protestantism and Authority," *Commonweal* (9 October 1964), pp. 69–70.

Chapter 14

1. John M. E. McTaggart, *Mind*, n. s., vol. 15, 1906.
2. Ibid.
3. William E. Hocking, *Types of Philosophy* (New York: Charles Scribner's Sons, 1929), p. 162.
4. Ibid., p. 163.

Chapter 15

1. Charles A. Bennett, *A Philosophical Study of Mysticism* (New Haven: Yale University Press, 1933), p. 100.

Chapter 16

1. William James, *The Varieties of Religious Experience*, 1st Modern Library ed. (New York: Random House, 1936), p. 396.
2. Durant Drake, *Invitation to Philosophy* (Boston: Houghton Mifflin Co., 1933), p. 34.
3. William Pepperell Montague, *The Ways of Knowing* (London: George Allen & Unwin; New York: Macmillan Co., 1925), p. 60.
4. William E. Hocking, *Types of Philosophy* (New York: Charles Scribner's Sons, 1929), chaps. 30–33.
5. Ibid.
6. James, *Varieties of Religious Experience*, pp. 370–420.
7. Charles A. Bennett, *A Philosophical Study of Mysticism* (New Haven: Yale University Press, 1933), p. 101.

Chapter 18

1. George Berkeley, *A Treatise Concerning Principles of Human Knowledge*, "reprint ed." (Chicago: Open Court Publishing Co., 1904), p. 40.
2. George Stuart Fullerton, *Journal of Philosophy*, vol. 22, 1925, p. 31.

Chapter 20

1. Bertrand Russell, *The Problems of Philosophy*, Home University Library of Modern Knowledge, No. 35 (London: Williams and Norgate; New York: Henry Holt & Co., 1912), p. 113.

Chapter 21

1. May Sinclair, *The New Idealism* (New York: Macmillan Co., 1922), p. 227.
2. William Pepperell Montague, *The Ways of Knowing* (London: George Allen & Unwin; New York: Macmillan Co., 1925), pp. 260–262.

Chapter 22

1. George Stuart Fullerton, *Journal of Philosophy*, vol. 22, 1925, p. 31.
2. E. S. Brightman, *An Introduction to Philosophy* (New York: Henry Holt & Co., 1925), p. 233.
3. John Stuart Mill, *An Examination of Sir William Hamilton's Philosophy* (New York: Henry Holt & Co., 1884), vol. 1, pp. 237–238.
4. Ibid.
5. Ibid.
6. J. B. Pratt, *Journal of Philosophy*, vol. 9, 1912, p. 579.
7. R. F. Alfred Hoernlé, *Idealism as a Philosophical Doctrine* (London: Hodder & Stoughton, 1924), p. 113.
8. C. I. Lewis, *Mind and the World-Order* (New York: Charles Scribner's Sons, 1929), pp. 64–65.

Chapter 23

1. Edna St. Vincent Millay, *The Goose Girl.*
2. Edna St. Vincent Millay, *Renascence.*
3. Ibid.
4. Edna St. Vincent Millay, *Euclid.*
   (The Millay quotations in notes 1-4 appear in *Collected Poems,* copyright 1956 by Norma Millay Ellis, and published by Harper & Row).

Chapter 24

1. F. H. Bradley, *Appearance and Reality* (London: Swan Sonnenschein & Co., 1897), p. 89.
2. A. E. Taylor, *Elements of Metaphysics* (London: Methuen & Co., 1903), p. 337.
3. William E. Hocking, *Types of Philosophy* (New York: Charles Scribner's Sons, 1929), p. 254.
4. H. J. Paton, *The Good Will* (London: George Allen & Unwin, 1927), chap. 3.
5. Taylor, *Elements of Metaphysics,* p. 342.
6. Ibid., p. 353.

Chapter 25

1. David Hume, "An Enquiry Concerning Human Understanding," *Hume Selections,* ed. Charles W. Hendel, Jr., The Modern Student's Library, Philosophy Series (New York: Charles Scribner's Sons, 1927), p. 156.

2. Ibid., p. 159.
3. Ibid., p. 151.
4. Ibid., p. 159.
5. Ibid.
6. Durant Drake, *Invitation to Philosophy* (Boston: Houghton Mifflin Co., 1933), pp. 272–273.
7. A. K. Rogers, *What Is Truth?* (New Haven: Yale University Press, 1923), p. 143.
8. William James, *Principles of Psychology* (New York: Henry Holt & Co.; London: Macmillan & Co., 1910), vol. 2, p. 671.
9. Ibid.
10. *The Grammar of Science* (London: W. Scott, 1892), chap. 4.

Chapter 26

1. Friedrich Paulsen, *A System of Ethics* (New York: Charles Scribner's Sons, 1899), p. 468.
2. Durant Drake, *Invitation to Philosophy* (Boston: Houghton Mifflin Co., 1933), p. 403.
3. John M. E. McTaggart, *Some Dogmas of Religion* (London: E. Arnold & Co., 1930), pp. 170–171.
4. William James, *The Will to Believe* (New York: Longmans, Green & Co., 1907), p. 171.
5. Henry Sidgwick, *The Methods of Ethics*, 4th ed. (London: Macmillan & Co., 1890), p. 74.
6. George Stuart Fullerton, *System of Metaphysics* (New York: Macmillan Co., 1904), chap. 33.
7. McTaggart, *Some Dogmas of Religion*, pp. 166–167.
8. Drake, *Invitation to Philosophy*, p. 409.
9. McTaggart, *Some Dogmas of Religion, p. 179.
10. Ibid., p. 178.
11. Ibid., p. 168.
12. Ibid., p. 173.
13. Hastings Rashdall, *The Theory of Good and Evil* (Oxford: Clarendon Press, 1907), pp. 321–322.
14. Ibid., p. 322.

Chapter 27

1. Chap. 10
2. Brand Blanshard, *The Nature of Thought* (New York: Macmillan Co.; London: Unwin Brothers, 1940), vol. 2, p. 312.
3. Ibid., p. 271.

4. Harold H. Joachim, *The Nature of Truth* (Oxford: Clarendon Press, 1906), pp. 72–73.
5. A. C. Ewing, *Idealism* (London: Methuen & Co., 1934), chap. 5.
6. G. F. Stout, *Studies in Philosophy and Psychology* (London: Macmillan & Co., 1930), p. 318.
7. G. Watts Cunningham, *The Idealistic Argument in Recent British and American Philosophy* (New York and London: Century Co., 1933), sect. on Bernard Bosanquet.
8. Blanshard, *The Nature of Thought*, vol. 2, p. 452.
9. Ibid., p. 304.
10. Joachim, *The Nature of Truth*, p. 104.
11. Blanshard, *The Nature of Thought*, vol. 2, p. 271.
12. Chaps. 11–15, 17.
13. Chap. 16.
14. William E. Hocking, *Types of Philosophy* (New York: Charles Scribner's Sons, 1929), p. 381.
15. Ibid.
16. William James, *The Varieties of Religious Experience*, 1st Modern Library ed. (New York: Random House, 1936), chaps. 16–17.

Chapter 28

1. Chap. 25.
2. From the Roman Catholic Mass.
3. Chap. 27.
4. Gen. 1:26–27, *The Jerusalem Bible* (Garden City, N. Y.: Doubleday & Co., 1966).
5. Rom. 12:4–5, JB.
6. Preface, Roman Catholic Mass.
7. Matt. 6:10, JB.
8. Acts 17:23–28, JB.
9. From Nicene Creed.
10. John 1:1–14, JB.
11. Chaps. 17, 18, 21–24, 27.
12. W. H. Moberly, "God and the Absolute," *Foundations: A Statement of Christian Belief in Terms of Modern Thought* (London: Macmillan & Co., 1913).
13. Edward A. Pace, *Catholic Encyclopedia*, s.v. "pantheism."
14. Chap. 24, etc.
15. Pace, *Catholic Encyclopedia*, s.v. "pantheism."
16. Ibid.
17. Ibid.

18. Ibid.
19. Chap. 26.
20. Pace, *Catholic Encyclopedia,* s.v. "pantheism."
21. Chap. 24, etc.
22. Ibid.
23. Ibid.
24. Chap. 27, etc.
25. Ibid.
26. Chaps. 5–7.
27. Moberly, "God and the Absolute," *Foundations: Christian Belief in Modern Thought.*
28. John Caird, *Introduction to the Philosophy of Religion* (Glasgow: James Maclehose & Sons, 1901), chaps. 5, 8.
29. Morris L. West, "Testimony of a 20th Century Catholic," *America* (2 December 1967), pp. 678–688.
30. J. A. T. Robinson, *Honest to God* (Philadelphia: Westminster Press, 1963), p. 86.

Chapter 29

1. Pierre Teilhard de Chardin, *Letters from a Traveller* (New York: Harper & Brothers, 1962), p. 24.
2. Pierre Teilhard de Chardin, *The Phenomenon of Man* (New York: Harper & Brothers, 1959), p. 297.
3. Ibid., p. 308.
4. Teilhard de Chardin, *Letters from a Traveller,* p. 150.
5. Pierre Teilhard de Chardin, *The Making of a Mind* (New York: Harper & Row, 1965), p. 93.
6. Teilhard de Chardin, *The Phenomenon of Man,* p. 259.
7. Ibid., p. 172.
8. Ibid., p. 30.
9. Ibid., p. 217.
10. Ibid., p. 251.
11. Teilhard de Chardin, *The Making of a Mind,* p. 241.
12. Teilhard de Chardin, *The Phenomenon of Man,* p. 308.
13. Teilhard de Chardin, *Letters from a Traveller,* p. 159.
14. Teilhard de Chardin, *The Phenomenon of Man,* pp. 284–285.
15. Teilhard de Chardin, *The Making of a Mind,* p. 277.
16. Ibid., p. 268.
17. Teilhard de Chardin, *Letters from a Traveller,* p. 274.
18. Bernard J. F. Lonergan, S.J., *Insight: A Study of Human Understanding,* rev. students ed. (New York: Philosophical Library, 1958), p. 425.

19. Ibid., p. 668.
20. Ibid., p. 212.
21. Ibid., p. 629.
22. Ibid., p. xii.
23. Ibid., p. 278.
24. Ibid., p. 191.